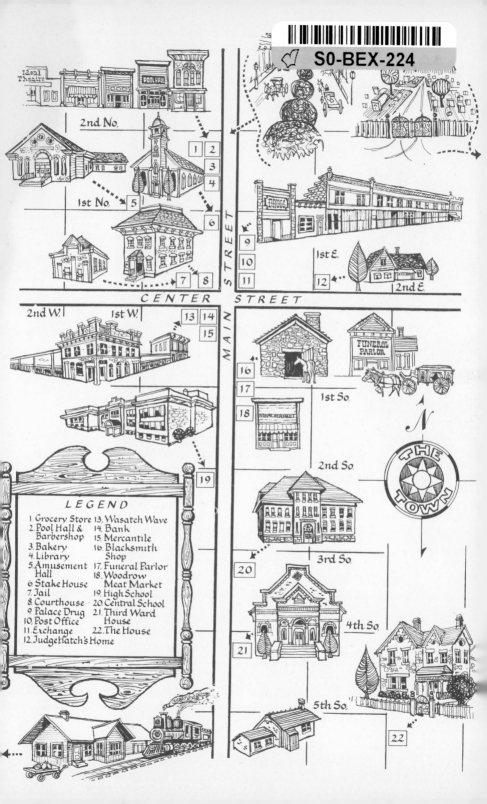

Ideal Theatre

POOL HALL

2nd No.

| 1 | 2 |
| 3 |
| 4 |

1st No. 5

6

7 | 8

CENTER STREET

DRUGS

1st E.

9
10
11

12

2nd E.

2nd W. 1st W.

13 | 14
15

MAIN STREET

FUNERAL PARLOR

16

1st So.

17

18 MEAT MARKET

2nd So.

19

N

THE TOWN

LEGEND

1. Grocery Store
2. Pool Hall & Barbershop
3. Bakery
4. Library
5. Amusement Hall
6. Stake House
7. Jail
8. Courthouse
9. Palace Drug
10. Post Office
11. Exchange
12. Judge Hatch's Home
13. Wasatch Wave
14. Bank
15. Mercantile
16. Blacksmith Shop
17. Funeral Parlor
18. Woodrow Meat Market
19. High School
20. Central School
21. Third Ward House
22. The House

3rd So.

20

4th So.

21

5th So.

22

A HOUSE OF

MANY ROOMS

A HOUSE OF MANY ROOMS

A Family Memoir

Rodello Hunter

· [Drawings by Roy Olsen] ·

NEW YORK / Alfred · A · Knopf

1965

L. C. catalog card number: 65-18753

THIS IS A BORZOI BOOK,
PUBLISHED BY ALFRED A. KNOPF, INC.

FIRST EDITION

For Emma, Kay, Gwen, and Phyllis,
who believed, and for the Family, who
polished up their memories
and brought them to me,
gleaming like Papa's Jonathan apples
in bushel baskets

THE FAMILY
Who lived in the House

DAVID WILLIAM WOODROW · *Papa, who built the House*
CATHERINE CAMPBELL WOODROW · *Mama, who kept it*
JUNE *and* JULY · *the first-born, twins*
PRILLA LOU · *the second-born*
TYLER · *the first-born son*
ROLLO · *the second-born son*
JOHN · *who lived such a little while*
MARY · *who did not live at all*
EMILY ELLEN · *who had Papa's eyes*
DAVID · *who wandered*
FRANCES *and* BOOT · *the first-borrowed*
MARYBETH *and* JEREMY · *the second-borrowed*
JEANNE · *the last-born*
RACHEL ANN · *the last-borrowed*
GRANDMA CAMPBELL · *who lived in the living room*
CLEMENTINE · *who stayed too long*

AND THE PEOPLE *who loved the*
Family that lived in the House

GRANDFATHER *and* MUZ · *who loved Grandma*
CLAY WINSTON *and* DUNCAN MITCHILL ·
who loved June and July
COLTON HANKS *and* DYKE PALMER · *who loved Prilla Lou*
MARGARET · *who loved Tyler*
ALICE · *who lost her way*
ANTONY ANDERSON · *who loved Emily Ellen*

And UNCLE LEW, *who took what did not belong to him;*
UNCLE JASON, *who was rolled up too tightly;* AUNT MAG
and AUNT SYBLE, *who could not live long enough;* AUNT
SALLY, *who was a little odd;* AUNT MARTHE CLEGG, *who
knew most of us better than most;* UNCLE JOHN, *who had a
big bark but no bite; and the rest of the people who lived
in our town.*

A HOUSE OF

MANY ROOMS

[CHAPTER ONE]

THE HOUSE told the story of the family. Papa had built it himself. He was carpenter and mason, glazier and plasterer. The house reflected his financial state and the growth of his family. Room by room, one at a time, he built, until it grew from a large, one-room log cabin into the white sprawls and peaks that all of us loved.

When the growing seasons were good and hay sold high, when he was city marshal, when his small herd of cattle thrived and he sold some of them at a nice profit, the rooms Papa built were large and paneled and high-ceilinged. There was a time when the family spilled over. The two big bedrooms looked like dormitories: Grandmother Campbell's ornate folding bed took up one wall in the dining room.

That was the year Papa built the little bedroom, and its one narrow window expressed his feeling of penury as he built.

All of the rooms were on different levels, and I have found no good reason for this way of building. When I questioned him, Papa just smiled and asked: "Why should all the floors be level? Folks have to watch where they're going in this house." I rather liked the jog up, jog down, as we ran from room to room. It was step down to the bedrooms, down to the little room, down to the kitchen and up again to the dining room and down to the parlor. Mama said those steps would be the death of her, and she spoke truly.

In most large families, if you look closely, you will find a chronicler. Ours was a large family. There were nine owned and five borrowed, as Mama said. While the others acted, I watched and recorded on a hidden reel of brain tape that went spinning on as the family grew and quarreled and played and loved. But there was more playing and loving than quarreling. Though I was "Critic," as Papa said, there was much more to praise than to criticize. The Woodrows were a breed of people who did not brood on sadness and who made excitement out of dullness. They made an event of the pulling of a tooth—the doorknob way, of course— and singing your first solo (whether you could carry a tune or not was of no import; it was the singing that counted) was an event that all of us remembered. I felt so proud when Papa praised mine.

"Look at that, will you?" he said. "She doesn't even come to the top of the table leg and listen to the lass sing!" My song was "We Thank Thee, O God, for a Prophet." Jeremy's was celebrated for years. He sang, with melody, "I am a Mormon Boy." He was four years old and he sang it standing on a chair in church. The solo, I am sorry to say, was his only major accomplishment for more than a decade.

The family began in the large, split-pine-paneled log room when Papa took Mama there after the wedding reception—or, rather, three days after the reception. That wedding, for those who believe in portents and omens, was probably indicative of the years ahead. And we most joyously did believe. Roosters crowing, except in the morning, meant company, and if you dropped a knife, they were coming hungry. I really don't believe that the knife dropping had much to do with it, for we never had any company that wasn't hungry, but that big old rooster never failed.

Papa and Mama grew up together, sat on the same benches in the one-room school (in turn of course; she was three years younger) and read from the same books. He teased the other little girls, but never Katie; and he didn't like it when her own brothers teased her. She never forgave him for snipping the tail of Aunt Sally's cat out of spite when she went to a barn dance with another fellow. I could hardly imagine Papa being so cruel, for I have watched those gentle hands so many times ministering to sick children and sick animals. When we discussed this bloody event, thoroughly, as we discussed everything, we decided that Mama surely must have given provocation. And "to give provocation was to merit punishment."

Both of them have told us about their wedding trip. Papa described the hill on which the Temple stood and how it looked down and over the valley, only a few curls of smoke whispering up from chimneys here and there. Later, many years later, when I stood on the same spot, it was over the roofs of a thriving community that I gazed and I tried to imagine it as it was for them. At the time they were married, the Temple in Salt Lake City had not yet been built and they had to journey from their small home town to Logan in a whitetop. Another betrothed couple shared the journey, and they stopped with friends at night. At each stop, on the way up and on the way back, there was a long and gay revel. They were met at the mouth of the canyon and escorted back home to their reception guests. So it was a tired and irritable bride and groom who finally came to the log house. "It was paid for, mind you, and the land it was put upon as well. None of this installment debt for the Woodrows."

Whatever they quarreled about, none of us ever knew, but Mama went home to her mother and it was three days before Papa, striding down the path in righteous indignation, went to claim his bride.

"Kate," he thundered (and that is no misstatement; Papa could thunder), "you are going to be my wife or you are not. Which shall it be?"

"I'll be your wife, I guess," she said sweetly, and she was. Once in a while she would arch her slender back and battle him. I have recorded one or two of these battles. She always won, for he laughed so hard that he had no strength to hold her from him.

For two years or more David Woodrow cultivated his land and Catherine cultivated her home. At twenty-four David was his own man. From the time Catherine Campbell's brown-bronzed locks and soft brown eyes had stirred in him a warm response, he'd been putting a little by against the day when he would ask her father for her. It took a long time. Although it was a prosperous mountain community, there was little money unless you were a merchant. A ticket to the Saturday-night dance was a bushel of potatoes or a peck of onions. Harry Miles charged a dozen, or somewhat, for a haircut, and traded to the Mercantile for foodstuffs, hardtack, and the bolts of dimity his wife liked to make up for her seven small girls.

Papa had a tireless back and strong arms. These he bartered for many months to get the section of rich valley land where he built for Kate. And the day he placed the deed inside his vest and buttoned the vest carefully, he marched up the hill and asked for a private conference with Grandfather Campbell.

The engagement lasted long enough for Papa to build the house. "When a man builds for himself (even if it is on many levels), he builds with care." It was long enough for Mama to acquire, with the help of her many sisters and Muz and Mother, six patchwork quilts and innumerable tatted, crocheted, and embroidered household linens. Grandfather Woodrow gave David, as he did all of his sons, a wedding gift of a team of horses, a saddle mare, and a twenty-dollar goldpiece. Grandfather Woodrow, by the county standards, was a wealthy man. Grandfather Campbell gave them a bedstead with a seven-foot-high headboard carved with cherubim and clusters of grapes. It had a high, carved footboard, too, with a flat top piece about three inches wide. Later, it became a test of skill, steadiness, and physical prowess to lie atop that footboard on your back for five minutes. There was a standing ten-penny prize for the insensate individual who could prove mastery over the bedboard. No one ever won it, fairly that is. Mama made Davy pay Jeremy because he stayed on three minutes before Davy tickled his foot. Jeremy fell off and hit the floor hard. But it was for the bruise that he was paid and not for the fortitude.

As was customary, Grandfather Campbell had to provide the wedding, and I am still struck with awe that after five other weddings he did so well. Weddings and funerals, then as now, were the chief causes for the gathering of the clans. In those days, when "Multiply and replenish" was still heeded as the first commandment, the clans were large and very willing to travel.

No one except the toddlers minded the plodding trips through the canyons, for though the roads were narrow, the vistas were not. Sharing the beauty and peace which surrounded them at every turn, the songs, the jokes, and the common crowded discomfort brought them closer to one another. Often as not, an all-day journey to a wedding produced another engagement and another cause for celebration.

It took five beeves, seven hogs, fifteen sheep, and uncounted chickens to feed what amounted to every able-bodied soul in the county. Mama clicked her tongue when she recounted that it used up most of one of Grandfather Campbell's ample straw stacks to provide mattresses for the sleep-over guests.

Grandfather Campbell would have been a wealthy man, too, if only his two wives had produced more sons and fewer daughters. For every time he got a fair start, one of his daughters married and this almost beggared him again.

Of course, every woman brought along enough to feed her own family and one more person. Fruitcakes wrapped in damp napkins to hold in the flavor, pumpkin, apple, mince, gooseberry, and custard pies, jellies, pickles, relishes, fruits in bottles, baked hams, headcheese, white-flour breads, cookies, homemade candies, pound pats of butter, and barley for coffee. Every inch of every wagon was filled. Decorated cakes, fragile cookies, and crushables were held on the laps of patient aunts and grandmothers, who protected them as they jolted along, so that they might arrive to be placed with housewifely pride on the host's table.

Muz and Mother Campbell could not depend on even their sizable flock of chickens to provide enough eggs when they would be needed, so for weeks they would put eggs down in water glass, a viscous liquid, to preserve them for later use. The egg yolks always broke and they tasted tired, but if they were used for baking there was no appreciable difference in flavor.

The Campbells' cellar was hollowed out of stone and earth beneath their house and it was cool. The milk house, built as it was over a running creek, was cooler, but creams and custards and potato salads could not be made long in advance. Kate's brothers hauled a wagonload of ice, packed in sawdust, from the icehouse down by the river, but it diminished rapidly between the wooden hand-turned ice-cream freezers and the avid children who kept queuing up to chip off "just one more piece, please."

It was to this happy confusion that the newly marrieds came. Catherine donned her wedding dress again and she must have been very beautiful, for fifty years later her eyes were still soft and brown and her ankles and legs were shapely. All of us have heard Papa tell Mama that she was beautiful and always I will remember the last time I heard him. They did not see me and I am glad, for I wept, and neither of them would have understood why.

All that day of their arrival they accepted the congratulations and teasing of their wedding guests, and then as children wearied and men thought of cows waiting to be milked, they began to take their leave.

Mother and Muz hugged Mama tightly as if she were going a long way for a long time. Papa drove out the gate with the reins held high and a wide grin on his face, while Mama (I can see them well) sat as primly as possible and as far away from him as her full skirts and the narrow seat would allow. If anyone could be prim under such circumstances it would have been Mama, even with some of the younger people following them, whistling and banging pans half the way home.

I have questioned them many times but the cause of their quarrel remained one of their many personal secrets. I never found out why Mama, in a whirl of rage and petticoats, jumped back into their borrowed buggy and drove quite capably all the way back to the flower-papered bedroom she had slept in all of her life.

She either sulked or reflected (I would guess it was the latter) during the time she stayed in her room and ignored the questioning of her sisters and brothers and the concern of her parents.

That David would come for her, she had no doubt, she told us, but there was still a spark of irritation in her voice when she said: "I must say he certainly took his time!"

The second time, she rode to her home in a rough-sided wagon into which Papa had carefully packed wedding gifts. He was gentle with the lovely pieces of china and cut glass and not one of them was broken, but he was uncommunicative and much less gentle with his recalcitrant bride. It was her brother Tom who helped her into the wagon, talking and laughing to cover her embarrassment. She moved meekly and did not have much to say, for she did not quite dare to strike a flint to the steel of David's visible wrath.

Although both of them were voluble about their courtship, their wedding, and the reception, the ride home must have been completed in great silence, for neither of them had anything to say of it.

I am very sure, though, that when he lifted her from that wagon and over the threshold, it was with respect and love and great tenderness, for these things he obviously gave her all of their years together.

[CHAPTER TWO]

Aunt Sarah had been watching out the window, and when she saw the wagon rolling slowly down the road, she ran out waving the bright blue of her apron vigorously.

"Dave! Dave!" she hallooed. "Hurry!"

Too far away to hear, he smacked Maud and Dick on their glossy rumps and startled them into a faster pace. He had put off going for wood as long as he could, for Kate's baby was due and she was such a little thing. She didn't seem to fear the event, but if she didn't, he did. When he imagined his family of sons, they were always in a family portrait. Six or eight of them at least, towering over their mother and, maybe, just a shade taller than he was. The youngest, a girl, would be sitting on Kate's lap.

Of course, he would adore the little girl, but a man should have many sons to help and prosper their parents in this world and to aid them in progression in the next. Vague fears sometimes twitched at him when he thought about that family portrait. But Kate was hardier than she looked, he comforted himself.

Papa wanted to be there at the birth of their first son. He knew when he saw Sarah, usually so calm and controlled, standing in the middle of the road, that something had happened. Probably the baby was near or had already come.

Aunt Sarah ran to meet him. The team, with their heavy load of wood, could not be pushed into a trot and she met him while he was still a block or more from home.

"You get on as fast as you can," she gasped, and clambered onto the high seat. "I'll take the team in." He dropped the reins into her hand and sprinted ahead, jumping the fence with only a hand on the top rail as he went over.

I got the story from them all and pieced it together.

When he rushed into the house, it was into a room that he had never seen before. It was full of women and soft flannel scraps and steam. Always the table had been neatly laid for a meal or just as neatly cleared, with its crocheted doily stiffly in place. Now it was stacked with basins and towels. Mother Campbell was lining the big wicker basket with warm, blanket-wrapped sadirons. Muz was holding a small blanket to warm over the stove, and she snapped at him: "Close the door! You want a draft to bring the death of pneumonia to these poor helpless ones!"

"Deliver me from women at a birthing," said Papa.

"They made me scrub myself in boiling water and lye soap. I could hear Kate whimpering and calling, but I couldn't see her for Aunt Marthe's fat behind and all the blankets they had strung up around the bed.

"Before I could get myself clean enough so Muz'd let me near Kate, I heard a squall and Muz said: 'It's a girl.' "

"I could tell he was a disappointed man," said Grandma Campbell, "but his face perked up when Aunt Marthe told him to wait a minute, there was going to be another one."

Muz wrapped the first baby in the blanket and brought her over to Papa. "My, she's a nice baby, Dave, and not near as much trouble as we thought there might be."

"This one is a girl, too." Aunt Marthe was chuckling. "Ye mighta knowed it. They got themselves twins, twin girls, and as pretty little things as you might pick of a kinnikinick tree."

"Twins!" Papa always recovered quickly. If he hadn't got a son, well certainly twins were the next best thing. Papa's pride bloomed.

"Aye, twins. The dear little girl done ye up brown. Now kiss her and then make yerself scarce whilst we set things to rights. My, my, wouldn't you know! The first twins in the county, and I'm the one that's proud to bring them."

I can hear Aunt Marthe and her brogue, and I can tell the story with a good bit of accuracy, for haven't I sat "a-listnin' " to her tell of the twins' birth and of mine and of the children that came after. The old midwife's brogue was so thick that every time I visited with her I carried some of it home with me, and Papa chided me for mocking people. I was not doing this, but it was hard to get back to "speakin' the English again for a bit."

Papa christened the twins June and July. Other names

had been chosen for them, but Papa capriciously changed his mind on the way up the church aisle. This was not the only time he was to do this. No one knew Tyler was going to be Tyler until he was named that after one of Mama's would-have-been beaus. June didn't mind her name and July put up with hers because, as she always said, she could have been named, and very nearly was, Samantha Mariah (pronounced Mair-eye-ee), after Papa's sister.

July was born with a bump on her head which was noticeable before her hair grew in. After she grew the thick honey-gold braids that Papa called the twins' crowning glory, no one could detect it. She was Papa's baby. If June woke in the night, Mama got up and diapered or rocked or fed her. If July had troubles, it was Papa who soothed them.

"But," Mama said ruefully, "June howled every whip-stitch, while, I swear, July slept each night through."

The babies were tucked in a big basket beside the bed and the lump on July's head made it possible for Papa to tell his baby without lighting the lamp; otherwise, they were so much alike that all of us got them mixed up. Their voices were identical, too, and they took advantage of it. While I was always trying to prove that I was a separate entity in a family where we were fitted into our places like stitches in a sock, they enjoyed all the confusion they wrought by being so alike.

When I was born, June and July were two years old and Papa added another big room to the original one. This was to serve as a bedroom and later, when the house had rambled all over the lot, as the parlor. That parlor was Mama's pride and my retreat.

High-ceilinged and thick-walled, it was a wonderful

place to read in. Even on hot summer days, the parlor was cool. I would lie on the tufted leather couch which, typical of our house, made out into a bed. It was a darkish room, and for some reason Mama seldom looked for me there. That was why I loved its austerity, which pushed the rest of the family into the rest of the house.

The walls were papered with a heavy, embossed extravaganza of gold and purple on a black background. The paper rolled up and up until it met a wooden border, which, I often thanked my stars, was too high for me to dust. Above that, the room stretched again into an expanse of white wall and then the ceiling, held up by a wide, intricately carved circle in the center. On it there were rosebuds and cupids, and it was always a wonder to me that any artisan could have put so much in the space. I was forever finding a new design and went to sleep many times still searching for an end and a beginning to this circle. From it hung a heavy chain and suspended from the chain was a lamp, like Joseph's coat, of many colors. It was made of dozens of tiny diamonds of glass which glimmered green and gold and purple. It was edged, too, with a deep metallic fringe, and it was probably quite horrible. But all of us thought that lamp was a creation almost beyond the ability of mortal man. When Jeremy wildly smashed the lampshade, there was not one of us who did not mourn the destruction of a great art treasure.

Always, as I read, I had company. On the wall were large, fancy gilded frames which held the silver-wedding-anniversary pictures of Grandfather Campbell and his first wife, Muz (her name was really Anne), and the later silver-wedding-anniversary pictures of Grandfather Campbell and his plural wife, Isobella, Mama's mother. Muz and Mother.

Muz and Mother, who lived together in polygamy. Muz, I did not know very well, for she died before I was old enough to manage easily the walk to her house. Mama and Papa went to visit them on Sundays. They often took June and July and sometimes Tyler, but I was usually left at home. No matter how I would vow to keep quiet and show my upbringing, there were so many questions to be asked. How else could I know which were my whole uncles and aunts, which my half? A half aunt! (I was nearly grown when I discovered that Mama's favorite brother, Tom, was really her half brother.) The involved family situation intrigued me.

Tyler was the fourth child. The birth must have been fairly uneventful, because, although Aunt Marthe Clegg delivered him, all she'd ever say was: "He was as nice a male child as you'd see anywhere. It was a relief to yer pa, I c'n say. He thought he was going to be like your Grandfather Campbell and sire a flock of girls." There was always a special note of pride in Papa's voice when he introduced one of the boys, though. At least, it seemed that way to me.

"Come over here, son. Brother Smith (or Lewis or Carlyle), this is my son Tyler (or Rollo or Davy)," or whichever farm-browned lad had wandered by.

July and I, with our noses out of joint when Papa had called over the boys and waved us into the background, went to Mama.

"Doesn't Papa love us as much?"

"Yes, he certainly does, but some men, most men I fear, feel that in their sons there is a measure of immortality. I suppose that's it. There are practical reasons, too, why men want boys. Boys are field planters and hay harvesters and a man can't hope to acquire much in this country unless he has help. Your Papa is one of those men. Be glad you're girls. I sometimes think Dave asks too much of his boys." This last she said with a sort of sigh, but I couldn't really tell. The dough she was mixing sighed, too, as she prodded and plumped it.

Rollo came just a year and a half after Tyler. The two boys were as different as June and July were alike. All of us were blue-eyed and fair-haired, but that was all the boys had in common. Tyler was slender and tall, slow-spoken and serious. Rollo was a roomful of sunshine. He carried with him a smile, a joke, a quick hug, and a generous heart and hand. When he was four and Mama was pinching pennies so hard that the Indians on them "were begging to smoke the peace pipe," Rollo earned for himself a much-needed suit of clothes by selling pins. Walking as far as his sturdy little legs could carry him in an afternoon, his round, bright face sold his pins for him as he unlatched the gates of the homes he visited.

"When I am big," he bragged, "I am going to have a house like Grandfather Woodrow's with a rooster on the roof and a spankin' team of bays like Uncle Orson has. I'll have all the rock candy I can eat and hire kids to do the hay trompin'. I am going to sit on the porch in the shade every afternoon and drink root beer. I'll bring you a chicken every Saturday night to cook for Sunday. Maybe even two chickens," he added generously.

He played hard, he worked hard. He laughed and loved with his whole being and he was beloved. Rollo was the one who sent money home so that Jeremy's sled was under the tree at Christmas that terrible year of 1918. It was he who bought June, for her wedding, the white silk slippers that neither she nor Papa could afford. Each of us felt that we were very special to him and certainly he was very special to each of us.

When I think of Tyler it is with a dragging sadness, yet it is with joy and inward laughter that I think of Rollo. I might have been a bit jealous of Tyler when we were small, for he was Papa's first son. Young as I was, I noticed that it was Tyler whom Papa always pulled to him first when he sang to us.

"Come Over Here, My Son," he sang. Over and over. He sang it to all of us, not only the boys. He sang it, too, to Rollo and to Boot, to Davy, especially to Davy, and last he sang it to Jeremy. I cannot remember ever being jealous of Rollo. He charmed us all, and even Papa could not resist his smile and his blandishments. Scots-English though he was, he must have passed by way of the Blarney stone on his pre-birth journey to us.

"We're getting a nice little family around us," Papa said. "And I'm glad that there is to be another. This one will no doubt be a boy to make things even. If I'd had my way, June and July would have been boys. It's always nice to have a son for the eldest child, to sort of oversee the others and take your burdens on himself, you might say."

"The twins are very lovely girls, and Prilla will be too, she's hardly more than a toddler. I really don't care what this baby is"—Mama's voice was a little sharp—"as long as it is all right."

"Well, you don't mind my hoping for another son, do you, Kate? This is a big farm and it's getting bigger. It's going to take a sight of hay haulers to get the summer work done about ten years from now."

"And it'll take a sight of kitchen help to feed the hollow-legged ones, too," she retorted.

"Hold up there, woman. I've never said I loved my sons better than my daughters. It'd be a foolish thing for you to think I do. Surely a man can wish for a son to even up the score!"

Papa's wish was granted. The baby was a boy but he lived only thirteen days. Papa held him in his two big hands and tried to comfort him when he whimpered, for that is scarcely all he did.

"His head is not as big as a teacup!" Papa mourned. "Such a little mite of a lad."

When the baby died, Papa grieved for him even longer than Mama did, although she was always saying her arms felt so empty. Papa bought a graveyard lot, a large one, big enough to lay us all to rest with "room to turn over," and the little grave seemed lonely and bereft tucked away in a corner of the barren ground.

Mama's arms were to remain empty yet for a while, for though the next year brought another baby, it was a stillborn girl. Except for shaking his head in bewilderment and saying: "She was as nice a healthy-looking child you could hope to see, she just didn't breathe," he spoke little of the loss. He laid this little one to sleep next to her brother and placed a headstone with a carved white lamb at the head of the two graves.

I loved that little lamb. On the days before Decoration Day, we would walk up to the graveyard and take care of the graves. It would have been shocking if the visitors that flocked in from everywhere to place flowers on the graves of their departed should find a Woodrow grave unkempt. We raked and pulled weeds and planted. It was my delight to carry buckets of water and wash the little lamb of its accumulation of dirt and bird droppings.

"If I die before I grow up," I asked Mama, "would you please put a lamb on my grave? Or maybe I'd rather have one of those little curly-haired angels like they have on Flora Power's leg. It seems kind of funny to have a headstone on a leg, don't you think?"

"The headstone isn't there for the leg. It's there for all the Powers' children. They've lost a flock of them, poor souls."

"It's right there, plain as day, right where they buried Flora's leg."

"You are a stubborn and obstinate child."

"I can show you. They thought Flora was going to die anyway, you know. They wanted to bury her whole so that it would be easy for her to reassemble in the First Resurrection. But she didn't die, and they'd already buried her leg in her grave. I wonder how it'd feel to come to the graveyard every year and put flowers on your own leg? Sort of like Captain Ahab, right under the ground waiting for you. Beckoning you on: 'Come on, Flora Powers, one fifth'— how much of you is a leg, Mama?—'maybe one seventh, of you is waiting. The worms are crawling in and out.' " I sang a few lines: "And the worms crawl in and the worms crawl out. They crawl all over . . ."

"Prilla Lou Woodrow, I'm going to take a willow and tan your legs for you good! It's a blessing and an answer to the prayers of the entire Ward that Flora Powers lives to put flowers on her leg. She's a dear, sweet child and a joy to her much-bereaved parents. I'll have no more nonsense from you, miss, and that's the word with the bark on it!"

When Mama said that, you had best be still, but I ventured carefully.

"She sure walks fine on her wooden one. You can't even

tell it's wooden. It's a good thing that they make legs nowadays, isn't it? How'd you like to go around on a peg? Thump-step, thump-step."

Mama slapped me, so I went and got another bucket of water and washed two lambs that were a couple of grave lots over. They were nice little lambs, but they'd been there a very long time. One had its ear eaten off by the wolves, I guessed.

[CHAPTER THREE]

When Emily Ellen was born, I huddled outside in the little clump of lilac bushes and bridal wreath that Papa had planted in a circle in a corner of the north lawn. The circle inside was large enough for three children to huddle in a hide-and-seek game or for one child to sprawl on a blanket and catch a slant of sunshine through the thick foliage on a printed page. We called it the Magic Circle and if you could reach its shelter, you were King's-Xed.

Aunt Marthe sent us to Aunt Jenty's, Mama's sister, for the day, but I didn't get into the wagon with the rest. I took my quilt and my book and hid in the Circle. From there I could watch the comings and goings. Grandmother Campbell came about noon, carrying a kettle of vegetable soup in one hand and her knitting bag and little Bible in the other.

Papa went in and out of the house, the slam of the screen door punctuating his quick steps. Even when Papa didn't go anywhere, he always went there fast. He chopped wood and filled the woodbox and stacked some against the corral wall. He worked in the granary shed for a while on the harnesses. From where I was hidden I could see him astride a sawhorse. He would bend his head to the straps and then lift it quickly to listen, then he would get the brass bucket and stop at the hydrant to fill it. He'd let the water run until it got its icy coldest and then take the bucket in to dump into the oval copper boiler on the stove to heat. He watered Maud and Dick twice, threatening them with a dry and choking death because they didn't drink much the second time.

He fed Mama's chickens and gathered the eggs, a job he hated almost as much as I did. There aren't many tasks as unpleasant as going into a feathery, warmy-wet, smothery chicken coop—to slip your hand down under the hen to get all but the glass nest egg. The hens looked at you so knowingly with their bright eyes, and all the time they were so stupid. They only pretended to be smart, cocking their narrow little heads to one side to dare you. The only times I liked chickens were when they were biddies and when they were cooked. Once I got spanked for gathering up all of one old hen's chicks in my apron and climbing up on the haystack with them. There was a little more to it than that, really.

The hen was clucking wildly and Mama came out. She asked me if I'd seen the chicks. I told her I hadn't and I put them underneath me, like the mother did, and sat on them. When Mama finally went in the house, I got up and all the fluffy little things were dead and draggled except one. It closed its eyes and stiffened in my hand as I held it. I didn't know what to do with them, so I covered them with some hay and slid down from the stack.

Papa discovered them when he went to feed the stock that night and Mama was sure mad at me. She made me get a willow and she took me outside in front of the kitchen window and tanned my legs and my bottom. I tried not to cry out loud because I didn't want the neighbor boys across the street to look up from where they were sitting on their porch steps. Mama was determined I was going to cry and I finally did. I couldn't hold the whipping against her; I knew it was merited. But I couldn't forgive her for quite a while because she did it in public.

Papa pulled me over on his knee after supper and said, all the while his hand was stroking my head: "It wasn't the loss of the chicks that your Mama was so angry about, Prilla. Sometimes even mother hens sit on their babies too hard and a chicken dies easily. It was the lie you told. You said you hadn't seen the biddies. The poor mother hen was frantic. You should have given them back to her."

"I don't like that old hen. She points her beak at me all the time."

Papa went on stroking my head.

"Those chicks you sat on, in a year or two, could have earned material for a pretty new dress for you. Ever think of that? And they could have earned June and July a new dress, too. The ones that couldn't lay eggs and earn money would have made Sunday dinners with dumplings. So you don't figure that you just sat on a dozen baby chicks, Prilla. The real loss was much greater."

I really felt bad about it then. I cried.

"I'm sorry," I said for the first time.

"But all that isn't the most important. The truth is always the most important thing. Remember, daughter, no one is smart enough to be a good liar; he has to remember too much that doesn't exist. And a bad liar is the most ridiculous creature on the face of the earth. Somebody always learns the truth and oftentimes the liar goes to his grave feeling that everyone is laughing at him. A man who is known to tell the truth will be believed under impossible circumstances, but a known liar will be doubted though he never err a jot nor a tittle from the truth."

He didn't ask me for repentance or reformation, but his slow, deep voice I can still hear. I may have been mistaken many times later in what I saw or in my interpretation of an event, but I told it as I saw it and Papa was right—truth rings as clear to the heart as fine crystal does to the ear.

Papa's lectures, and we received them individually, were always difficult to endure and wonderful to remember. This was only the first of the many I received. Once I swiped chocolates from a box that had been given to Papa for his birthday, and when he went to bring it out to treat company, he found that "only one more" and "only one more" soon emptied the box. It hadn't looked that way to me.

"My," he said, amazed, "those surely went in a hurry!" He left the lavender box on the table, where it kept looking bigger and bigger through the evening. After the company had gone, he sought us out, Tyler and Rollo first, then the twins, and finally me. He sat on the side of my bed.

"Did you eat all Papa's candy?"

"Yes," I said staunchly.

"Didn't you feel you had your share with the others?"

"Yes. But I wanted more. I liked it."

"Mmm. How would you feel if I found your Christmas stocking and ate that without asking?"

"You wouldn't!" I was deeply shocked.

"You did. It was about the same, don't you think? The candy was for my birthday."

"I'm sorry, Papa. I'm really sorry."

"I'm sure you are, Prilla. And because you are so sorry, and because you must not really have thought you were getting your rightful share so you had to steal it, I want you to look at the pieces that are left." He opened the box and carefully picked out the brown crinkled empty dishes. "I want you to take the biggest one in the box."

"Oh, no, I couldn't, Papa. You eat the rest. You can punish me anyway you like and I won't be mad at you."

"This is your punishment, Prilla. You are to pick the very biggest piece."

I hesitated with my hand over the box. "Not that one, the other piece is bigger."

I took the candy thinking Papa's punishments really had no sting.

"Eat it."

"Now, in bed?"

"Now, while I watch."

I couldn't nibble the chocolate, enjoying it as I had secretly nibbled and enjoyed the others. I stuffed it into my mouth and chewed and swallowed and almost choked on the sweetness.

"Would you like another one?"

"Oh, no, sir!"

"Good night then, Prilla."

He closed the box and pulled the covers up around my

chin, and though I wanted a drink of cold water to wash away the sickening sweetness of the chocolate, I did not dare to ask him to bring me one, and he did not bring one to me when he came to bed, as he did most nights. Papa's punishments may not have had the sting of Mama's willow, but to this day I cannot buy a box of chocolates if they come wrapped in lavender paper.

The hours that we waited for Emily Ellen were even longer for me, I think, than they were for Papa. He kept busy. I watched him as he mended a slat in the fence, staked up the columbines, and planted another row of green peas in Mama's vegetable garden. He found some rusting sadirons in the shed and polished them brightly and hung them for weights on the gate, so that it would not swing shut when we went through with our arms full. It was a task that Mama had been asking about for quite a while. From the woodpile he selected a likely pole with a fork at the top and sat on the kitchen stoop and smoothed it down to make a clothesline pole. He firmed the supports on the clotheslines and restrung the rope with a role of wire I am sure that he originally planned for another use.

Mama would be pleased. She was proud of her white wash and she hated the rope lines. He found some paint in the pantry and stirred it, evidently to paint the poles, but there was not quite enough. It was obvious that Papa didn't want to leave to go after more. I kept very still, for had he known I was there he would have sent me downtown to get it.

The hours dragged on and finally Papa, forced to remain near and forced to keep busy, began cleaning out the raspberry and gooseberry patches. He cleared out the tangles and made narrow little alleys between the bushes. This would help when we had to pick them.

Grandma came out and brought him a bowl of soup and some thick-sliced homemade bread and butter. There was a dish of green onions and new radishes and a tall glass of milk. I was hungry as I watched him eat but I could not come out.

He put the dishes inside the door on the washstand and listened for a moment, then he went back to his raspberry bushes. He was hoeing the weedless garden when Grandma came to the door and called.

"The baby is here, Dave. It's a little girl." Not practicing what he preached and putting it away, Papa dropped his hoe and hurried through the garden gate.

He went inside and I followed him slowly. I could not stay in the Circle any longer. There was no one in the kitchen and the living-room door was shut. I couldn't hear the baby crying—only the rumble of Papa's voice.

Grandma came out and saw me standing by the stove.

"Well," she beamed, "you've got a little sister. Would you like to see your mama?"

"Could I?"

"Of course you can, dearie. They're both right as rain, right as rain." She poured hot water from the teakettle into the washbasin and scrubbed my face and hands with a soapy cloth as though I were a baby. Then she dried me rather roughly and led me into the living room.

Papa was sitting by the bed with Mama's hand in his, and Mama had Emily Ellen tucked down beside her. Emily Ellen yawned and mewed sort of like a baby kitten and Mama had tears in her eyes.

Aunt Marthe Clegg bustled up. "I'll take the wee lass now," she said. "My, look at the little fuzz curls around her ears, and her eyes are big and all-knowing. This one is going to be a heart smasher. Aye, that's for certain."

"Oh," crooned Mama. "She feels so good against me. It's been so long since I held a baby." Then she became very solemn and said: "I pray to God, Dave, that this house will never be empty of children."

"Ayee!" Aunt Marthe wailed as she heard Mama's words. "What have ye done, Kate? What have ye done? God and His angels are so near the newborn, they've most likely heard yer words. Ayee! I hope you do not live to regret them. This I do." She made motions with her white apron as if to shoo away the wish-granting angels. Then she took up the sleepy baby to tuck her in the big old basket that had been bed already for six Woodrows and yet showed little wear. Papa mended, stained, and varnished it like new before each one came.

We didn't birth any more babies for a while, but we got them just the same. Papa built two more rooms. They were big rooms, too, and the only two rooms that were on the same level. We had a bedroom for the girls and a bedroom for the boys. Papa would have saved a lot of confusion if he'd left out the connecting door. I have always been sure that the noise we made, if it were piled in a heap, would have put that old Big Bertha gun to shame. There were water fights and pillow fights and there is not one window in either of those two bedrooms that has not been replaced many times. When it was possible to fix blame, the culprit paid breakage, but most of the time the deed had been done by no one, and until Papa could find time and money to put in the pane, we put a white-painted cardboard in the square. We saved it between times.

Someday I shall go back, perhaps even before I have chronicled all the Woodrow history, but this I have decided. I shall go back and knock upon that door in the house and ask the strangers who live there if I can come in. I will see for myself if the bedrooms and the parlor are as big as I remembered them, for time has an odd way of ballooning the past and squeezing the present.

My first memory is of the bedroom that later was my serene, cool parlor. I walked into the room, and I cannot remember what room I left behind me. This was Mama and Papa's bedroom. I kept my hands behind my back because I was not supposed to touch the glass box that held Papa's stick pin and the little gold buttons with which he held his shirt cuffs together. I was not supposed to touch the man and lady who held each other closely on a porcelain bench. There were roses, pink and perfect, and someone had picked a few and scattered them around the lady's feet. I wanted so much to see if I could pick one off, but Mama slapped hard when she slapped your hands. If you were really bad, she sent you for your own spanking willow. I always chose the slenderest one I could find and didn't know for some time that those were more wiry and stung worse than the big ones.

I looked. It was one of the few quiet times that I remember. There were no sounds in the house, except creaks that came only when no one was home. The lowboy with its mirror stared at me and I saw myself looking, and approving that I didn't touch.

I looked for a long time and I got tired. The door was

open when I had come in, but it had swung shut behind me. The thousands of sharp metal eyes that patterned Mama's milk safe winked at me. She kept the milk safe in her bedroom because we did not have a milk house built over the creek like Grandfather Campbell had. Our creek was just outside our fence and I could hear it there now, noisily detouring around the rocks and roots which stopped the water from flowing smoothly down the hill. I thought some about dipping my finger in the thick yellow cream that stretched tautly across the top of the low, flat, round pans. It was nice to lick, but I could see from where I stood that the knobs on the milk-safe doors were even higher than the one on the door from the bedroom, and I couldn't reach that.

I walked around the room. On the wall was a picture of June and July with their blond hair curling loose to their shoulders. The picture was tinted and they wore soft gray-velvet dresses with red collars. They sat on a tiny, narrow bench and hugged each other tightly as though they were afraid of something big and staring. The picture was set in a five-inch frame of gold curlicues. When I saw them I remembered the song Mama sang: "Oh, do you remember a long time ago, lived two little children whose names I don't know. Were stolen away on a bright summer's day and lost in the woods, the story does say." The song went on very sadly about the poor lost babes in the woods who sobbed and sighed themselves to death. I sobbed, too, when she sang it, but it was my favorite song and I always asked for it when it was my turn to choose.

June and July looked like the poor lost babes in the woods. I wanted to see the picture closer, so I tried to climb up on the bed. Since that time I have always easily identified myself with the Lilliputians in *Gulliver's Travels* and I knew

exactly how Alice in Wonderland felt when she shrank. The
bed was so high that I could not pull myself up on it. I tried
and tried, but only succeeded in pulling the crocheted bedspread down to drag untidily on the floor. I was very tired
and so I sat down on the braided carpet and cried a little,
softly, for the room made my wails sound bigger than me
and I was afraid.

Mama must have been outside gathering eggs or on some
such brief morning errand, but it seemed that she was gone
for a very long time. Then I lay down on my back and
looked from there. The bed on one side blocked off my view
but elsewhere the walls climbed endlessly. The paneled
closet which filled one wall and one corner seemed more
than big enough to hide the giant of "Jack and the Bean-
stalk," and the full-length mirror which silvered up from
Mama's lowboy reflected more walls and more ceiling.
There was so terribly much of everything and it was all so
big. How could anyone as small as I was ever be found? I
wondered. I had lost me.

[CHAPTER FOUR]

Papa was the vocal member of our family. He was always preaching sermons on Sunday evening, and when he was speaking, all of us, if it was possible, went willingly to hear him. We went, not because he was such an interesting speaker, although he repeatedly told us that his Patriarchal Blessing said that he would have a tongue like as to the pen of a ready writer, but because he was an old-fashioned revival speaker. His voice rose and lowered and he pounded the pulpit. That Blessing was certainly true. He never lacked for a word or ah'ed or and'ed, and the chapel rang as he preached. I have often wondered what the rest of the congregation thought, but I imagined him standing there in the raw goatskin of Elijah or John the Baptist or the blood-and-thunder favorite Isaiah, and I enjoyed it thoroughly, especially the night that Candida Caldwell broke up the meeting. I told Papa afterward it was because he shouted so loud that he weakened the ceiling, but he didn't think I was very funny and called me "Critic."

That was really a night to remember. Candida was a child with an angel's face and an imp's soul. No one looking at her could bear to accuse her of any sort of mischief and so she was never punished, even though she sold as many setting hen's eggs as we did and skipped school, rolled her underwear up, too, and used makeup. Most of the time it was Dede who thought up the things the rest of us got punished for. But if there was ever a public confession and retribution, it was poor old Dede's. From that night on, everyone of us felt sorry for her.

The Caldwells always made their children go to church. They loaded them all into a whitetop and brought them three times each Sunday. We went quite often, nearly every Sunday. One meeting, Papa said, was enough sitting for any child and we could take our choice of Sunday school, afternoon meeting, or Sacrament Meeting. We nearly always went to Sunday school, because all of the kids went and it was very nice. We were told Bible stories and most of the boys had to go, so you could usually see the one you liked best. When Papa spoke, we always went, and as there were few Sunday nights that he was not the visiting speaker in one Ward or another throughout the valley, we were quite regular attenders.

Candida was not impressed by Papa, and somehow, this night, she had slipped away with three or four other kids and gone up into the forbidden steeple. It was dark up there and they were walking along the narrow rafters. Suddenly in the middle of a roaring "and there descended from the heavens . . . ," there was a crash, and plaster rained on the people in the center aisle. Hanging weirdly from the ceiling was one very long, black-stockinged leg. Dede had slipped from the rafter and crashed through the thin coating of plaster.

I guessed Mrs. Caldwell recognized the leg, for she screamed, and Mr. Caldwell rushed for the stairs. Poor old Dede was bawling, you could hear her down in the chapel. She was cussing, too. There are people who said, and still say, that it was someone else, not dear Candida, who did it. When her father rescued her, she was hanging for dear life on the rafters on each side of her and trying not to follow her leg through the hole.

It took a while to get the hole patched. They made ceilings nearly inaccessible then, and though the volunteer plasterers did a fair job, the mark of Dede's transgression is still there, plain to see. It stayed with her, too. I don't think her folks did anything to her except make her apologize for interrupting Papa's talk, but Dede repented and reformed, and I am very sure that that reformation cheated her out of the rest of her normal childhood.

If Papa was the preacher, Mama was the storyteller. She had inherited Grandma's gift for mimicry and all the Scotswoman's flair for dramatics. We loved her stories even though she told them again and again.

On nights when Papa was out churching or marshaling, Mama would often gather all of us into her featherbed. In the unheated bedroom we would cuddle down to our chins under her comforters, turn out the lamp, and listen. If the ghosts that she brought to life were to return on dishwashing nights, at least on storytelling nights I was enthralled by them. She told us, through her stories, of the settling of the valley, of the Indians, of the Manifesto and the trials it brought, and of her own little-girlhood. It is always so delightfully unbelievable that your grown mother who wielded authority with a willow stick and who could say "you will" and "you do," was once a child subject to some of the same tribulations that we knew. It was comforting to think of that.

Mama's stories were wonderful and we chose them in turn, like we did the songs. When it was my turn, I alternated between the one about the Polygamist's Sons and the Day of the Dog.

All the people in our little town were related one way or another. What happened to the Campbell family, Grandfather Campbell's brother's family, was as important to us as our own. Human relationships colored our days and provided entertainment. Mama's stories, while abiding strictly to the truth as she knew it, were exciting. There was the story of Uncle Joseph Campbell:

Uncle Joseph was a small man. At full height he did not rise to Grandfather Campbell's shoulder. He was older than Grandfather and had lived in Scotland when he was a boy. He had to work very hard and for long hours, and maybe it was all that work that stunted his growth. But though small in stature, he was powerful in every other way. He had a deep, melodious voice, the gift of healing, and an inspiration for loving. He married when he was very young and the marriage was a happy one. Two years later, he married his wife's younger sister. After that marriage, which was also happy, he married four more times.

In the years that followed, Uncle Joe's wives had thirty-seven children, twenty-two of them sons. The sons, while hard workers, were well nourished, and the smallest, as was common for the Campbell clan, was over six feet tall and weighed more than two hundred pounds. At the time of the Manifesto, the law which abolished polygamy among the Saints, Uncle Joseph was a grandfather many times over and there was not a runt in the lot of his posterity. I'm not sure how many there were, but counting sons, grandsons, and sons-in-law, the little old man was able to command a sizable stand of men. They owned a big ranch and they held family horse-breaking and calf-roping contests that would cast a blight on most rodeos. All the boys were fair hands with a horse and gun, and people of the valley felt safer, during the Indian rumblings, because the Campbells lived at the entrance to the valley. It could well be that this was the reason we had no violence when over the rest of the state there were tales of murder, theft, and kidnapping. The Indians trailed peaceably through our valley, offering no enmity.

The new law, the Manifesto, said that all of the brethren who had more than one wife would have to cleave to one and sever the rest. Many men refused to separate themselves from their plural wives and their families, so they served terms in the State Pen. (When Mama told the story, I knew nothing of prisons, except bits I'd read in Alexander Dumas, and with Mama's words I saw a big pen, something like a sheep corral, that the men wandered around in.)

Marshals were hired to bring in the offenders and, for the most part, the men went peaceably, though protesting, in to serve their sentences. Two husky, armed men were sent out to our valley to pick up Uncle Joe and take him back to Salt Lake City. When they knocked at his door, he was expecting them and welcomed them. He packed his saddle-bags and mounted his horse to go with the marshals. But as he rode down the street, all of his sons, sons-in-law, and grandsons, armed with rifles, were waiting on horses at the first turn. There was no show of violence. No man raised his gun. The boys fell in behind the marshals and their father as they had done many times in the Independence Day parades, and followed him through the town and out of the valley. No one spoke. The sun rose high and it was hot. The dust rolled up from the horses hooves; the only sounds were those made by the river as it rippled and rushed, the wind, and the birds in the trees at the side of the road.

Although there was not one raised gun, the marshals must have felt that menace, as well as ridicule, rode behind them. What explanation could they make when they rode in with an innocuous little gray-haired man, followed by an army of armed giants? This keg of dynamite could blow up in the faces of the authorities, and the marshals did not want to be guilty of lighting the match.

Halfway down the canyon they called a halt to the procession, turned Uncle Joe over to his sons, and shook hands all around. The marshals told Uncle Joe that any man who could sire his own army shouldn't spend time in any State Pen and, that being as good a reason as any for his release, he rode back to the valley and the marshals returned to Salt Lake City.

The authorities down there must have thought the marshals used good judgment, because no one ever came out again to get Uncle Joe. For that matter, that was the last time there was any trouble over polygamy. Most of the polygamists were pretty old by then and the young men hadn't taken plural wives, so as the brethren died, so did polygamy.

The other story that I always chose was one of the

"in the olden days when you were a little girl, Mama" kind.

Grandfather Campbell raised sheep and the livelihood of his family rested upon them. The settlers depended on friendliness and handouts to keep the Indians peaceful. The Indian chief Tabiona was thought to be tottering between the generosity of the people and the threats of Black Hawk to join in war against the whites. Tabiona, with his braves and his squaws, his meager possessions piled on their travois, trailed through Grandfather's ranch periodically.

Every time Tabiona was in the vicinity Grandfather lost sheep, not all of them by theft. The Chief had a big gray dog—a wolf dog, the children thought—that killed the sheep wantonly. At night he would sneak into the sheep pens. In the morning sometimes as many as eight of the animals had their throats torn away. Mama began formally:

"Old Dad McDonald lived in and helped Grandfather with the work. The older boys were just beginning to be of good use on the ranch and Grandfather, like the other men of the valley, traded work. If there was a barn to be raised, everyone helped, and usually all it cost the builder was the makings of a barbecue and the price of a fiddler at night. At threshing time, then as now, the men worked together, field by field, until all the crops were harvested. Old Dad was a one-eyed wanderer, who came sick and hungry to our door one night. His horse had died two ridges away, and Muz and Mother took him in to nurse him until he was well. He was always a bit of a mystery. He was not a Latter-Day Saint, nor would he ever join the Faith, but he defended our right to it with a zealousness that few of our own men displayed.

"It was about time for Tabby to come through our territory, and Old Dad set himself to watch. Perched on the shed roof above the sheepfold, he hunched over his gun in the cold spring night. There had been a heavy dropping of lambs and Old Dad loved the lambs.

"About midnight, he saw a gray shape slipping up through the willows, and he knew that it was Tabiona's dog. The dog was alone on his raid. Old Dad raised the gun to his good eye and as the dog sailed over the fence and crouched to spring at the throat of the first victim, the shot exploded in the night.

"I heard Father slam the kitchen door as he ran down to the corral, and before Mother could get into her robe and get the lamp lighted, the older boys were into their clothes and grabbing their guns. They followed Father on down the hill.

"Father came rushing back to take the kitchen door off its hinges. 'Old Dad has shot Tabby's dog, and if he finds it out, he might cause some trouble,' Father told us."

With the Black Hawk War sporadically breaking out, the threat that an unhappy Tabiona might take his braves and join Black Hawk was no little one to scattered and comparatively unarmed families.

"Mother dressed us and we were all given things to do. Muz mixed a huge batch of dough and Mother rolled out crust for gooseberry pies. I went down to see what Father and Old Dad and the boys were doing.

"They had placed the body of the dog on the kitchen door and gathered up all the dirt around the spot where he fell. Then they dug a hole in front of the barn door. They put the dog and the dirt into the hole and the older boys were set to cleaning out the stables, at two o'clock in the morning. They scraped and cleaned and washed all the manure from the barn out the door and over the grave. Father turned the horses into the corral and ran them around and around until all trace of new earth was lost and trampled under their hooves.

"While Father and Old Dad brushed all the tracks away, tracks that might lead the Indians to the sheep corral, Mother and Muz washed the kitchen door with lye water and Father rehung it.

"By six o'clock, at sunup, all of us were sitting at the breakfast table. Muz's bread was in loaves ready to bake, and Mother's pies, a dozen or more of them, were fresh from the oven on the sideboard.

"We'd had family prayers, all of us kneeling at our chairs around the breakfast table, and Father's voice was strong and unafraid as he prayed for help in dealing with the Chief. Then we had the song for the day. Father had a beautiful singing voice and he sang: 'Fear not, I am with thee. Oh, be not afraid. For I am thy God and will still give thee aid,' All of us sang, and though I was still too scared to eat much breakfast, I felt better.

" 'They're coming, Father,' one of the boys said. 'Several horses, I'd say, to make that much dust.'

"Old Dad followed Father to the porch. He carried his gun, which he had just finished cleaning.

" 'Put the gun in the corner,' Father told him. 'Just sit easy and when Tabby comes, I am the only one that will talk. All of you keep still.'

"Tabiona and three of his braves rode their horses up to the porch. Four other Indians had dismounted at the sheep-fold and were looking intently at the ground around it. When Tabby's shadow fell through the open door and onto the breakfast table, Father rose and raised his hand in the peace sign, which the Indians ignored.

" 'Tabiona look for dog. Dog here much. Where dog?'

" 'You mean the big gray dog?'

"The Indian grunted, looking around the room as though we might have hidden him there.

" 'I saw your dog last night, and I saw him the day before about sunup, but I haven't seen your dog running around today.' Father was telling the truth. When he had seen the dog, it was dead.

" 'Dog not here?' The Chief looked at Father and we knew that he didn't believe him. I had crawled with Jenty and Sarah under the kitchen table and we watched him through the lifted tablecloth.

"Tabby went to a corner of the room and took Old Dad's gun to smell the barrel. Then he took the three other guns from the rack on the wall and sniffed at those.

" 'More guns?'

" 'No more guns.' Father turned up his hands to show that they were empty.

" 'Chief like hot bread?' asked Father, but Tabby turned around.

" 'Look for dog,' he said, and he went out of the kitchen and down the porch steps.

"At the sheep pens the other braves had sifted some of the dirt through their fingers and were looking into and around the shearing sheds. One of the Indian dogs picked up a scent. He rushed frantically about and the Indians watched him closely, but he came back to the fire that Old Dad had started, right over the spot where the dog had dropped.

"The Indians searched everywhere. They looked in the stables, walking over the dog's grave to enter and come out. They looked in the mangers and in the hayloft. They went out into the pasture and looked for evidence of digging. They searched under the porch and examined the well. Chief Tabby demanded that Muz allow him into her cellar and he poked among the potatoes and carrots she had stored there from the previous fall. He ignored us as we crowded again under the kitchen table and he did not seem to notice Muz or Mother or the older boys.

"The Indians bunched together and talked and gestured and finally scattered to go over the place again. The sun's rays slanted down and settled on a bright object on the ground near the shed on which Old Dad had sat when he shot the dog.

"Father and the boys sighted it almost at the same time. The discarded shell from Old Dad's rifle! If the Indians saw that shell, they would know that a gun had been fired. And cartridges weren't just thrown about. They were remelted, cast, and filled to be used again. Tabby was smart. He would know!

"It was a miracle that the Indians hadn't found the bullet case as they searched, for moccasin prints patterned the dirt of the shearing-shed floors. The Chief approached Father, and he must have caught the drift of fear that Father was trying not to show. The shell glittered in the sun. Tabby looked at Father. His eyes were slits and he ordered still another search of the sheds and the ground around them.

"Old Dad, canny old man that he was, anticipated the Indians' surge toward the shearing sheds. He walked through the gate in front of them. Father willed Old Dad away from the dangerous bit of metal, but Old Dad walked directly toward it, and Chief Tabby, wary now, walked behind him.

"Hadn't Old Dad seen the shell? Father was certain that

he had. If he had, why was he walking straight toward it and death? Father watched, horrified, as Old Dad bent over and picked up the bright object from the dust.

"Tabiona held out his hand, silently demanding. Father knew that a dash for the house was useless. He had no weapons and they were outnumbered. Poor one-eyed blundering Old Dad had done for them all!

"Old Dad stepped forward, squinting in the face of the Chief, and opened his palm. As the Indian stared, Old Dad nervously shifted his weight, the heel of his leather boot grinding deep into the soft earth.

"Father walked slowly up to Old Dad and the big Indian. As he came closer he saw what the Chief was looking at. It was an almost new horseshoe nail. Gravely, Tabiona handed the nail back to Old Dad. He went out of the gate and, motioning to Father, started up the slope in an easy run to the house.

" 'Bread,' he said.

" 'Muz,' Father called, 'put all the bread in a flour sack for the Chief.' He took the sack of still warm bread and added, from the cupboard, a jar of honey and a slab of salt pork.

"Tabiona took the sack, grunted, and, moving easily across the porch, jumped on his pony. He rode away, his men following him down the grassy slope.

" 'The Lord be thanked,' said Mother, and we gathered with such relief around her to watch him go.

"At the bottom of the hill, Tabby pulled his horse up and, turning, raced it back toward the house. He slid off the horse and bounded across the porch and into the kitchen. Reaching a long, naked arm in front of us, he took a gooseberry pie and carefully removed it from the plate. He gave the plate to Muz with a smile and then, holding the pie in one hand, he mounted his horse easily and loped down the hill, greedily eating as he rode."

After that story, I always felt just as I did after Thanksgiving dinner, full and contented and ready for a nap.

Mama's stories were so detailed that usually one story a night was all we could hope for before we heard the noisy opening of the kitchen door, which always stuck and seemed to burst into the kitchen each time it was opened. We knew that Papa was hanging up his hat on the rack behind the door and that he would be removing his coat as he came through the bedroom door.

Tyler and Rollo were always asleep when he came and he took them from the foot of the bed and carried them to their beds. I don't think they ever knew how the stories came out. Oftentimes I was so sleepy that he had to help me to bed, and many, many times I would remember the end of the story, but be surprised to find myself in my own bed the next morning.

"Did Papa carry me to bed, too?"

"No, you went by yourself."

"I don't remember."

I never remembered. I always went to bed, I guess, sound asleep. This was the nicest way because I didn't wake to feel the bed icy cold, to lie and shiver although my feet were pushing against the hot bricks that Mama always put in our beds on winter nights.

[CHAPTER FIVE]

THE YEAR 1901 was the year of the Mission. I guess word of Papa's tongue, like as to the pen of a ready writer, had gotten out as far as the Church Authorities, because Papa was given a Mission call to the Southern States. Emily Ellen was five months old and there were June and July, Tyler, Rollo, and me filling the house as full as one of Mama's pickle crocks.

"I have absolute faith in God, Kate," said Papa. "He never lays down a burden that he doesn't give the strength to bear, and the Lord will provide." Well, the Lord, with the aid of Mama, did very well, and Papa with his quick and jaunty step was off for two and one half years to carry the Faith to the unenlightened.

To go on a Mission in 1901 was to have the boldness of a Crusader and the faith of an Abraham. I always think of Mama when I hear the story of the valiant woman who, crossing the plains in a handcart, looked at her exhausted husband in sympathy as he shook his head in despair at fording a stream which rushed before them. "I'm finished," he said, "we'll never make it across." She fastened up her heavy skirts and went to the rear of the cart. "Come on, John, you pull and I'll push. Before you know it, we'll be on t'other side!"

While Papa fulfilled his Mission, Mama both pushed and pulled on her treadle machine. She supported the family by sewing for people in the town and she did an unprecedented thing for a Woodrow. She bought a sewing machine on time. For the one and only time, she ran her face, as Papa would say.

When Papa came back to find the crock just as full (only the pickles were bigger), Mama had paid for that sewing machine, fed and clothed her family, sent Papa money each month, and had thirty-two dollars in the bank. She was a small and modest woman; the task must have been herculean, but I never heard her complain.

It was a time of work for all of us. June and July and I had acquired a regular job. Uncle Will Warrington had the first real screen theater in the valley. Of course, there'd been traveling lantern shows before that, but it was enterprising Uncle Will who brought the jerkily tragic and fast-moving heroes and heroines into our lives. As Uncle Will would obligingly accept a dozen eggs or some such for a ticket when you didn't have money, the movies were a popular nightly diversion.

All of the Woodrows sang from the time they could talk, and Uncle Will asked June and July if they'd be the sound effects for his shows. I played the piano well enough to accompany them and he hired all three of us for fifty cents a night, six nights a week. The money we dutifully turned over to Mama; in fact, Uncle Will paid her himself every Saturday morning.

Every other morning we'd meet the early train, get our sheaf of music, which came along with the can of film, and go home and practice so that we could accompany it that night. Erma Jensen was an accomplished pianist and she did the horses, the thunder, and the posse's-after-the-villain music, but we did the songs and the rest. If the singer happened to be a man, July just poured out a little more alto and I guess we were a moderate success. I say moderate, because when Papa came home and could take over the finances again, Uncle Will hired some new sound effects.

It was fun at first, but after a while the practicing got to be drudgery. The songs were simple and fortunately we had good ears for music. When I think of it now, Mama must have been a monument of patience and deafness, for she treadled hundreds of miles on that old machine through all our practicing and never made any except helpful comments.

I tended Aunt Maggie's kids for five cents an hour. And she stayed square hours. But they were nice little kids. There were three of them, Elizabeth, Boot, and Frances. Aunt Mag always stayed so long that I was weary and cross when I finally got home. She lived all the way across town and it seemed sometimes that all I ever did was walk.

Walk to the butcher shop, walk to deliver some sewing,

walk to Aunt Mag's, walk downtown to get some thread, walk to the library, and finally every night, except Sunday when we walked to church, we walked to Uncle Will's theater. There was never a mortal soul that hailed the invention of the motorcar with the joy that I did. Bicycles were popular and many of the kids had them, but though we wanted one more than anything else in the world, we never did get one. When Papa was on his Mission we could not afford the money to buy a bike even though we earned it. The day Papa brought us one piled on top a wagonload of flour was one of the saddest and most remembered days of our lives.

Rollo, only four, sold pins, and while his contribution was small, so were his needs, and he was earning his salt. When he wasn't canvassing the town and winning the heart of every female, of any age, with his bright face and smile, he took care of Emily Ellen.

That wasn't really a task. She was the softest, cuddliest, purple-pansy-eyed baby you ever saw. I never got to hold her enough. While we practiced she sat in her cradle and crowed and applauded. On the days when the songs wouldn't come right and Mama had trouble with tucks and gussets and ladies who bulged in places hard to fit, Emily Ellen was our joy. I know that some folks clucked when they heard that Papa had accepted the Mission call and was leaving Mama with five children and a little baby. They seemed to think that the baby would be burden, but, oh, how she wasn't. She was our real, live doll.

We picked gooseberries by the dozens of quarts. Rollo complained of the googles that stuck him and Mama would pick the thorns out of our fingers at night. Gooseberries are terrible to pick. They are too sour to enjoy popping one into your mouth and it was prickly torture to force your way into the matted bushes. By the time we had filled our pails, we were scratched, our hair was awry, and our fingers were sore and bleeding.

Once, June and July got an order for twenty-five quarts at five cents a quart from Aunt Ide Johnson. They delivered the gooseberries on schedule but Aunt Ide never paid them. That money was planned for their new school shoes. I went with one or the other of them two or three times to dun Aunt Ide, but she was always "just fresh out of money." "You should have come a little sooner," she would say. I hoped then and I hope now that if by some mischance she makes the Celestial Kingdom, she has to eat gooseberries for all eternity.

Mama made delicious gooseberry pie, everyone said. She took prizes all the time at the county fair. I wouldn't know whether they were good or not. I could never stand the sight of the nasty little green things from that summer on.

Next to Mama, I think this time was hardest on Tyler. When Papa boarded the train, Tyler became a man. Eleven years old, he took over all the farm chores. He was up at four to milk the cows and feed the chickens and horses. He plowed the garden with Old Maud and later, after he'd worked and weeded and raked, he dug furrows with a hoe while Mama dropped in the seeds and we covered them up with our hands. He dug the potatoes, too, while we came behind him and turned over the clods of earth to get every precious last one to store in the root cellar for the winter. My shoulders ached with the bending and I wondered how Tyler, big and tall for his age though he was, could do all that much harder work.

He chopped wood and filled the woodbox, though July often went out to help him. In time, she could wield that ax pretty well for a girl, and she wasn't a very big girl.

The Elders' Quorum harvested our hay. Grandfather Woodrow had died the winter before Papa's Mission, and Grandfather Campbell was ill and unable to do more than walk, puffing, up to our house and back to his.

June took over one of the *Deseret News* routes, and every night except Sunday she delivered papers before she came home to get ready to sing at the showhouse. I rode with her behind the saddle several times. She'd rein the horse and I'd have the paper folded to toss on the porches or put in the mailboxes. Of course, there were the fussy souls who had to have their paper in certain spots, and to keep in good with the paper and the subscriber, one of us had to dismount and walk the paper to the door. No lady wore pants, and being a lady was one damned nuisance. I swore every time I slid, with my skirts going skyward, off that horse. Finally, June stopped taking me because she said my bad language ruined her appreciation of what, she said loftily, were the beauties of the world around her.

In the winter it took all of us, even Rollo and Mama, to deliver the paper. Mama would put the baby on the sled in a box and she and Rollo would take the houses nearest home while the rest of us broke up the farther parts of the route, so that we could get back in time to make first curtain.

Uncle John Woodrow, grouchy and cross, was a big bear of a man. There was one black cow that Tyler, despite all his stubborn struggles, could not milk. You practically had to immoblize her to milk her, so rather than kill the cow (nobody would buy her), Uncle John came down every night and morning to milk her. You could hear him cursing from the barn if you dared open the kitchen door, and he threatened her with bizarre forms of death every night.

When I think back, my heart aches for that tall, slightly stoop-shouldered boy. Tyler didn't laugh and joke like Rollo, but he never complained and he was never cross. When something bothered him he chopped wood.

We sang, and Mama sewed. June and July and Emily Ellen, when they were grown, turned out to be quite domestic and did unbelievably intricate and beautiful things with their needles, but I would think of the piles of cut materials and boxes of thread and newspaper patterns and any urge I ever had to sew would come to naught.

There was another way that we made money. This, too, was a family project and it was quite remunerative. Tucked away in the corner of one of Mama's magazines, which she couldn't afford to renew, was an ad. "You can have your loved one's face on your pillow," it said. You could get a photograph, send it back to the company with a dollar and seventy-five cents, and they'd send back a pillow cover, either satin or velvet, with the picture printed onto it. We sold a lot of these at two dollars apiece. June and July carried on a thriving business. All the girls they knew, and small towns have flocks of unmarried girls, would put their lights of love on the pillow. They were remarkable for poor quality and bad taste, but, oh, how they sold!

There were other people who helped, too. In almost every letter that Papa wrote, there'd be a word of thanks to the Bishopric or the Relief Society or some widow lady like Betsey Blackley (who wasn't a member of the Church) for sending Papa a dollar or two in a letter. We, in turn, must take a pint of cream or a peach cobbler or a dozen cookies to the giver to show our appreciation. I was glad that Rollo had a good sense of direction. He combined pin selling and thank-you deliveries, and I must say that no salesman ever had a better pitch.

Uncle John (the bear) Woodrow and his tall thin wife (she looked like one of the Wyndham sisters in the painting by John Singer Sargent) did the most, I think. Although Uncle John would greet us with a growl when we entered his butcher shop to buy a ten-cent soup bone, we never left with that soup bone. We had beef roasts and mutton chops and ham hocks and ground beef.

We welcomed bread and milk for supper and we never once thought that was all there was. As Papa had asked, the Destroying Angel passed us by. None of us had so much as a cold, though you'd expect it, sloshing about delivering papers and cookies and pins through snow sometimes up to our knees, or higher, depending on how tall we were. But no matter what our trials and tribulations, every letter that Mama wrote Papa went something like this:

MY DEAR DAVID,

We are all well and hope you are the same. The baby is fine. She says "Daddy" (this was to Bishop Duke, who picked up our uncarryable purchases, such as flour, and delivered them, and who called upon us weekly to see if we were in need of succor) and walked across the kitchen floor today. Her eyes are deep blue like yours, Dave. She has hair like your mother's.

June and July are fine girls. Prilla Lou shows a little too much sauce and she reads too much. She is going to ruin her eyes and cause us to buy her glasses, I am certain.

Tyler is the man of the house. Without him, I do not

*know how I could manage, but with him and the help of
the rest of the family, we are doing very well. The Lord is
ever near us and sends us friends whenever we are in need,
as I hope that he will also with you.*

*Rollo is my fine little man. I am sure that he is going
to be wealthy, for he manages to slip as much as twenty-five
cents at a time into my apron pocket. He never gives it to
my hand nor mentions it, but he climbs into my lap and
hugs me tight. And then when he is gone there is always a
few cents in my pocket for his "share." I think that he is
Mother's favorite. But her indulgence does not seem to
spoil him.*

*The days are passing, but they go slowly. I will be
glad when you have accomplished your duty toward the
Lord and are back safe with us once again.*

*I hope that the sister you mentioned—did I read you
right, Wilmina Horsie?—finds her way clear to go into the
waters of baptism and she surely will. It makes me sad that
you had to walk so many miles to find a place to accom-
modate you. I wonder for the state of the world that anyone looking at your good face could think that you were
other than one of the finest of men.*

*Enclosed you will find ten dollars. I hope that it does
not find you too much in need of it.*

> *With much love from us all,*
> *Your wife,*
> CATHERINE CAMPBELL WOODROW

I never saw Mama write a letter. She always wrote them
at night when the light was too poor for sewing and we
were asleep, but she left them for us to add kisses and hugs
and any notes we might wish to the end of her pages. June's

notes always said something like this: "I went sleigh riding with Dick Jones. He is a nice boy. Of course, all the rest of the Sunday-school class went, too."

July's: "Mama made each of us a new dress just alike. It is plaid, trimmed in white. Mama says it is the Campbell tartan."

Mine: "I just finished reading Elsie Dinsmore. What a wonderful book! It is so sad. I cried buckets. I am going to read it again, maybe twice, before I take it back to the library."

Tyler's: "I am fine. How are you?"

Rollo's: "xxxxxxxxxxxxxxx oooooooooooooooooooo."

[CHAPTER SIX]

WHEN MAMA received the letter from Papa telling her that he had been released and that he would be coming home within the next two or three weeks, she sat down in the rocking chair and cried. All the time he was gone, she'd never shed a tear, and now that the time of the sewing and the singing and the gooseberrying and the paper delivering was nearing an end, she let down. We were startled and embarrassed, and not adult enough to understand her tears, but she didn't cry for long. No. She housecleaned.

When Mama housecleaned, she took everything up,

down, off, and out. We papered and painted. We scrubbed and waxed. We used vinegar water on the mirrors and the windows to make them shine. The rugs came up and were taken out on the lawn to be scrubbed and to dry in the sun. We even varnished the wooden rings that supported the front-room drapes on the rod Papa had carved for them. From the attic to the cellar, everything was to be prepared for the Great Homecoming. Even the jars of fruit were dusted and rearranged on their shelves. We laid new carpet pads of fresh straw. Mama washed all the wedding china and put it back in its place in the china closet. Blankets, pillows, bed ticks were washed or aired. There was not a whipstitch of anything in our house that was not polished. Things never meant for you to see your face in, you saw your face in. No wonder women were old at forty. Methuselah could not have been more weary than I when I fell into bed at night. All of this in addition to the regular money-earning duties, because we had to send coming-home money to Papa, and Mama was bound and determined to have the sewing machine paid for and "a bit for Dave to draw on when he comes home."

We were on the last bit of cleaning, putting the polished furniture back on polished floors, when Papa's shadow fell across the room. Tall and grinning, there he stood framed in the doorway. I hadn't remembered that he was so big, but then Papa always looked much taller than he really was because of the way he wore his hat. New hats were rarer in Papa's life than new shoes were in ours and he treasured them.

"Papa, why don't you crease your hats down in, like all the rest of the men do?" June urged him, but he looked at her in disgust.

"What's the use buying a new hat and then ruining it by punching the top of it in?" His philosophy about airplanes and his philosophy about hats were identical. If men were meant to fly, they'd be born with wings; if hats should be creased, they'd be made that way. He wore his always, straight on his head, high and domed and freshly brushed.

All of us ran for Papa except Emily Ellen. Mama cried for the second time and Papa patted and oh'd and ah'd at how big we were and kissed us all and nobody wanted to do any more work.

Papa reached for the baby, and Emily, three years old now, scrambled onto the couch and backed, big-eyed, away from him.

"Who's dat man? Go 'way, man. I don't like you enny more!"

"It's Papa, baby, it's your own papa," we told her. But our loving little one was wary and aloof. She had been the center of attention too long to enjoy taking a back seat to this high-hatted newcomer.

No matter how Papa cajoled and coaxed her to come on his knee and ride the cocked horse to Banbury Cross, she stared at him coldly and rejected his offers of friendliness and his horehound sticks.

Mama felt bad about the baby's rejection of Papa, but she felt even worse for him when, at Bishop Duke's appearance, Emily Ellen ran and laid her little face against his knee. "Hi, Daddy Duke," she yodeled. "I will give you a big kiss and a hug!"

Despite his pleas, Emily ignored him until one day when she stomped her red-shod foot and told him: "No." At our house, no one, not even the baby, said "No" to Papa. Ever.

He was mending a halter in the kitchen, and he asked her to hand him a bit of rope just out of reach.

"Hand Papa the rope, that's a good girl," he repeated.

"No," she said flatly.

"Hand me the rope, Emily Ellen." His voice was firm and I looked around from my breakfast dishes.

"No. Who bought dat damn rope into iss damn house!"

With this, she stamped on the rope and kicked it. Papa reached out, grasped her with one big hand, and swung her over his knee in one smooth turn. He smacked her three times on her round behind and set her firmly down.

She stood there looking at him and the big tears welled from eyes exactly like his.

He held out his arms and she ran into them, sobbing, and he loved her and fondled her and told her Papa's little girls didn't say "No" and they didn't say "damn" and Papa loved them very much. So he won her, and that was one of the two times that I can ever remember her getting a spanking. I could not tell you, though, how many times my legs have been tanned or how many times I've been swatted briskly or thumped on the head with Mama's thimble. Thimble pie, she called it, and often gave you a choice of punishment: Upshag, downshag, kick, cuff, or box. An upshag was having your hair jerked sharply upward; a downshag, the hair was yanked down hard; a kick was a kick; a cuff and a box were about the same; and, of course, you could always choose thimble pie.

If the Lord had stayed the hand of the Destroying Angel (as Mama had told Papa in one of her letters while he was on his Mission), He let it fall on Papa's return.

After Papa's official homecoming in the Ward House with all the brethren and sisters congratulating him, and his giving of the official report of the Mission, things were supposed to settle back into the old normal grooves, except that they didn't.

First began the plague of sicknesses. All the measles and mumps and chicken pox we hadn't had while Papa was away caught up with us and, turn about, we had them. For almost a year, one or another of us was down with something. Mama kept her sewing machine in the front room and sewed and nursed whoever happened to occupy the blocked-up sickbed.

Dr. Alexander's buggy was hitched so often at the front gate that after the siege the horse just naturally turned in our way whenever he passed our street going home. Once the doctor fell asleep and the horse was finishing off Mama's sweet peas when the doctor woke up at two o'clock in the morning.

The sickbed hadn't been out of the front room for a week when Aunt Mag died in childbirth. They had moved only a few months before out to the dry-blast reservation country and I guess they didn't have an Aunt Marthe Clegg, for she had died. Aunt Maggie was Mama's favorite sister. The feeling between them was sort of a warm glow that spread out and enveloped everyone within reach. If Mama had problems, they were Aunt Mag's, and I'd baby-sat for her a lot of times and been paid, to find out later that she was home helping Mama get out some rush order.

When Uncle Lew brought the two little ones to us, Mama and Papa welcomed them gratefully. "It's the least we can do for Maggie!" Mama mourned that we weren't given the oldest girl and the new baby, too. But Uncle Lew had taken nine-year-old Elizabeth to his sister, who wanted a child who could be of some help to her, and the doctor knew a childless couple who wanted to adopt the baby. Glad to be so easily relieved of his responsibility, Uncle Lew quickly assented.

"I don't know why I didn't tell Lew we'd take them all," Mama cried. "Breaking up Mag's family like this. It's a shame! I just thought he knew we'd help out." But the arrangements had been made and Aunt Maggie's husband was in no mood to listen to a change in his plans, so Mama was grateful for four-year-old Frances and two-year-old Robert, always to be Boot.

For a few days, the new little ones wandered about, hand in hand, not crying, but looking like another set of my babes in the woods. There was too much activity going on about them for this to last very long, and with the ease of butter melting into potato soup, these new babies melted into our family. They were the first of the borrowed children who filled in the gaps in our family like second teeth in the mouth of a seven-year-old. Once, in fact, an owned baby was taken out of her warm bed in the middle of the night for a new borrowed brother to take her place.

Emily Ellen was five now and as pretty as Aunt Marthe had predicted. Her hair was goldy brown and curled off a wide brow. Her lips were red and pursed slightly and her nose was small and sweetly tipped. Her eyes, purple-blue like Papa's, were one of only two pair I've seen that color and I've never seen her smile without bringing forth a smile in return. I envied her voice because it was low and carried chuckles in little cadences as she talked. She was captivating even when she was mad and, like Mama, she was mad frequently; but also, like Mama, she was so small her rage didn't frighten anyone much. We were more inclined to smile at her.

Mama had been complaining that Boot, at four, was getting too old to be the baby and so it was no surprise to us when she took to wearing gathered front aprons nearly all the time. She had stopped sewing for people, except for a few of her most faithful customers. It took nearly all the time she could spend at the machine keeping us all dressed and mended. She was sewing for the new baby, too, and it was fun doing catch stitches on the little kimonos. There is something about baby clothes that sort of caresses your heart, if you are a girl, that is. I don't suppose baby clothes cause much response, except a little embarrassment, in men. At least my brothers, well aware of the coming baby, ignored the obvious signs of it, but Papa didn't.

When Grandma made a shawl of hairpin lace, alternating rows of pale pink and blue yarn on her clever big hairpins, he was appreciative. "Fine enough for a prince." He admired her talent with her needles and often praised her.

Papa's little prince, when he came, made a rather surprising and unobtrusive entrance. It was a Mutual night and we had hurried the evening chores so that we wouldn't be late for church. When we left, Mama was sitting quietly at the kitchen table writing a letter of congratulations to Aunt Sally, who was the last of her sisters to marry.

For sometime, Aunt Sally's independent state had been a considerable worry to Grandma and to Mama. She was working in Salt Lake City and doing very well for herself, I judged by her pretty dresses and flowery hats, but now she'd found herself a man. She was about thirty and spoke of herself, fondly, as an old maid. But she was no old maid. In no time at all she was married and she had seven children before she was forty. Of course, she had two sets of twins and that increases the family numbers rapidly. I always liked her, and though it seemed like she was just starting to have, was just having, or had just had a new baby, she was surely cheerful.

"Z.C.M.I.," she would shout as she swung open our gate with her brood stringing out behind her. "Zion's Children Must Increase!" Aunt Sally had some extremely odd ways, and though at times I was assigned to be her constant companion so that no more than a reasonable number of Mama's linens found themselves mysteriously in Aunt Sally's drawers, I loved her very much. She had cheerful odd ways.

That Mutual night, though, we came back to find Mama in bed and little Davy snugged away in the newly varnished clothes basket. But if his birth was uneventful, that is about the only thing about him that was. From the time his eyes could focus, he was looking for new worlds to conquer. The world in a little farming valley isn't really very large, and there's not much roving to be done in it. I guess if people are born to rove and wander, they do it. Itchy feet, they say, but I think it's more truly some sort of combination of willing feet and searching heart.

Papa poured out his love on this little boy. Not that he neglected the rest of us. He loved us all and we knew that he did, but it seemed that he loved Davy just a little bit more. I guess that he knew he did, for he was more strict with Davy. He was "going to be taught to tread the straight and narrow."

All of us were introduced to this Biblical path, but nearly all of us were allowed a little falling away with not much said. If June and July danced until midnight, often they were given just enough of a morning nap so that they "couldn't possibly get ready for church on time," and then, of course, what was the use getting those tired girls up? A Sunday morning's sleep could do them the world of good. Tyler and I faithfully went. Tyler went because Papa expected him to appear in Priesthood meeting without fail, and I went because I was in love with Charley Updike, who led the singing. Being in love with Charley was wonderful. I just sat there and sang my heart out because he led the music. He was the handsomest male I have ever seen. Unlike most love affairs, it was painless. Anesthetized as I was by his appearance and abilities, I never dreamed that he would ever ask me to go out with him, and he didn't. But for at least two years I had a perfect attendance record. The only one in the Sunday school. Papa and Mama were very pleased with me. "Prilla Lou deserves a chalk mark on the wall," Mama said. Rollo, often as not, wasn't anywhere around when the rest of the family started off to church and he got by with it because no one, not even Papa, could be stern with him.

"Yes, sir, you're right, Pa," he'd grin. "I know, I know, but," and the excuse was always plausible and logical and he charmed the displeasure from Papa's face and went that night to hear him preach.

"That was a right fine sermon, Pa. I'll bet you'll never live to count the converts you made on your Mission. Just like the pen of a ready writer. Pa, you should have been a salesman; you'd sure been a whizdinger."

Rollo called Mama, Ma, and Papa, Pa, and got away with it. I remonstrated with him. "It's countryish and undignified and disrespectful," I told him. "Call them Mother and Father, Sir or Ma'am, or Papa and Mama as the rest of us do."

"It's all right, Critic," Papa said calmly. "Rollo can call us Ma and Pa if he wants to. You remind me of the Si Joneses.

Aunt Mary Ann used to say: 'When Si and I have children, they are going to call us Father and Mother. Nothing else! There'll be none of this Pa and Ma business in our family.' Well, after a while they had a family grown up enough to talk, and you know what those children called their parents? Mud and Pud." Papa threw back his head and laughed joyfully. "Mud and Pud! And they never did get over it. Why, only last summer, with their eldest boy old enough to help with the haying, I heard him call his father Pud. No. I'd rather settle for Pa and Ma." So Rollo called them Ma and Pa, as did Jeremy when he came along, but except for those two privileged ones, we were expected to speak to our elders with respect and, oftentimes, if we had company, only when we were spoken to.

"Children should be seen and not heard" was a child-rearing tenet in our family, and upon later observation, I think it is an excellent one. While we felt our importance and were always praised for our good qualities and chastised in private for our bad ones, an adult, any adult, came first.

Dinner waited for Papa's arrival at night. If he was late with the chores, or if, when he was marshal, he was called away on business and not back at the usual suppertime, we waited supper for two hours before we were allowed to eat without him at the head of the table. When we had adult guests and there was no more than enough butter to serve them—and Papa, of course—Mama would nip each one of us in turn. "Caucanny on the butter," she'd whisper, or the whipped cream, or the pie, if the company was numerous and unexpected, and she had counted on one serving apiece. And we caucannied.

When there were twenty-three for dinner and the table seated sixteen, we waited our turn. June and July and I waited with a little more dignity, because we served, but the smaller children were sent out to play, or into the parlor with jackstraws, to wait until the grownups had eaten and the table was cleared before we ate. It was a way of life, and as we were used to it, we would have felt out of place and awkward if we had been included at the first table. When finally you sat down before the children you realized that you were on the other side of the bridge, you were grown up.

[CHAPTER SEVEN]

O NE OF THE CHIEF FUNCTIONS of the human brain seems
to be figuring out ways to lie to itself." Papa expounded on
polygamy, but only at the kitchen table or while you
washed the dishes, never in the pulpit. There, he stuck to
Faith, Repentance, and Baptism.

Polygamy had always been a target for criticism and bitterness. While he was on his Mission, Papa told us, the first
question he was usually asked was: "How many wives do
you have?" His answer, "As many as I can support," may
have seemed sauce for the gander, but in a case or two it got
him run out of town by men bent on mayhem.

"There I was, thinking of no other woman but your
mama, and these men wanting to splinter me into kindling

because they thought I'd taken for myself something they'd like to take. More than one of them had a back-street wife and unacknowledged children. At least the men who practiced polygamy lived with their wives openly and cared for their offspring. Not that I hold to it, even if the Prophecies do say that the time is yet to come when seven women will hold to one man's coattails."

"You think polygamy is going to come back?"

"What else would you interpret that prophecy to mean? But never fear"—he winked at Mama—"I think that polygamy was one of the greatest trials ever devised to test the character of man!"

"Women." Mama contradicted succinctly from her rocking chair.

After the Manifesto there were some bitter choices made, but Grandfather Campbell dared the wrath of the law and refused to separate his two wives. When he became too old to work the ranch, he lived with them in town in a big house divided by a long hall that led to the first "modern" bathroom in the county. On each side of the hall the rooms were identical except for the furnishings, which were each wife's choice. Not long after the legal abolishment of polygamy, Muz died and Grandfather no longer divided his hours. He and Mother lived together until he followed Grandma Muz to the resting place on the hill (they had a high, pointed spire for their headstone; I never could reach the top to wash it), and Grandmother was left alone. She was getting along in years and though she was firmly independent she was lonely in the big house. Papa and Mama moved her into our front room. From her place of respect here, she supervised the length of our hair, hems, and hours that boy callers could visit.

"Our men have fortitude," joked July. "If they'll brave the wilds of Grandma's watchful eye, we know their intentions are honorable." Neither of the twins seemed to mind their chaperon; rather, they'd coax her to talk or sing, for her Scots brogue was charming and her sense of humor as broad as her sense of seemliness was deep.

No one ever complained about Grandma's living in the front room. She had brought all her favorite, and massive, pieces from the town house and the ranch and she lived surrounded by her tall cupboards, her ornate folding bed, her china closet, filled with the exquisite blue dishes and cut glass, her little black rocking chair, the huge, high-backed rocking chair that had been Grandfather Campbell's favorite, her footstools, her round table, her square table that had eagle-claw feet which grasped large, shiny red-glass knobs, her seven-foot-high elaborate headboarded bed, with its carved and entwined footboard. It took me over an hour to dust inside all the little curlicues. When Emily found out how much I hated that dusting, she offered to do it for me and did it so well and lovingly that I did not even feel guilty about passing the dirty duty on to her.

Now she was Grandma, not Mother. Her face was papery soft and wrinkled with tiny lines that sprayed out over her cheeks. Emily loved to run her fingers down the lines and count them, and the little one with a scratch or a sliver or hurt feelings was usually to be found cuddled on Grandma's lap, eating one of the cookies she always had hidden away for just such an emergency.

She would rock away in her little black rocker, with its round, padded wooden arms and its high tapestried back, and sing. Odd little songs that have caught in the recesses of my memory. There was "White Felither O Lay."

Whether that is really its title, I cannot be sure, but that is how it sounded and now it seems a tiny bit risqué to be sung by such a straight-laced little old lady. It went like this:

> *There was an old woman in Yorkshire,*
> *In Yorkshire she did dwell.*
> *She loved her husband dearly,*
> *But another man twice as well.*
> *Singing White Felither O Laro*
> *White Felither O Lay.*

Accompanied by the simpering gestures of the perfidious Nancy, the Yorkshire woman, and the sly Jimmy, the husband, "White Felither" was my favorite Grandma song, although she sang others from which I remember only snatches. Like: "You are old, Father William, the young man said." And it went on to something that she chuckled over when she sang, about the old man standing on his head when the young man could not. When she sang it, it rhymed.

The "Old Father William" song, one day, brought on one of Papa's periodic tests of skill and ability.

By now, June and July were piling their hair atop their heads, wearing stays and suggestions of bustles, and having brave young men call on them. Then I came, then Tyler and Rollo, little Emily Ellen, Frances, Boot and Davy.

This bright, blue-skied morning, Emily Ellen was dusting and Grandma was trying heroically to teach me how to knit. She was singing the "Old Father William" song when Papa came in. He managed a daily visit with Grandma and she adored him. "It takes a man to really brighten up a woman's day, be she six, sixteen, or sixty!"

After a while, as though he'd pondered the thought for

a long time, though I know that it had suddenly occurred to him, he said: "Prilla, you round up everybody. We are going to have a family contest."

Papa's contests were fun. In a time when just about the only entertainment available to us was an occasional Mutual Improvement Association dance, we learned to make our own joys. We had more fun at our house than any other place in town. Papa was always in the midst of it, for, like Peter Pan, he never grew old. When he complained years later that age was a creeping in his veins, none of us really believed him.

I gathered up the twins from their sewing and Mama hallooed for Tyler, and Rollo, picking raspberries, was glad for a respite from woman's work.

"I have decided," said Papa sonorously, "that . . . if any, or all, of you can beat me in a race around the block, I will take over all the assigned chores of the winner, or winners, for one week. We start at the corral gate. I will go left, all of you will go to the right. There are no penalties if you should lose. Agreed?"

We agreed and out we trooped, Grandma and Mama and Emily Ellen coming out to judge.

At Mama's "Go," we started. I looked back to see Papa's long legs striding around the corner. Already the boys had started to run and were yards ahead of the rest of us. (I forgot to say that participation was a rule. At our house, if the rest of the family ran races, you ran races. It wasn't that you were forced to run the race; it was just that you usually missed out on something if you didn't.)

That was a mighty big block. I saw July looking over to see the top of Papa's head midway up the block on the other side. She bent down, pulled off her shoes, and started to run in earnest. She began to set the pace. The boys, ahead at first, had to pound to keep their lead, and as we passed Papa, he ignored us while we derided him. We were just a hair-breadth ahead of him, I thought, but his stamina held out. By the time I limped, puffing, around the last corner, I could see him grinning widely at the boys, who were stretched out on the bank of the ditch. July had come in first of the kids and June and I had trailed in last. Papa, they said, had been waiting when she rounded the corner, her hair streaming down in back, minus one slipper she had dropped and wouldn't stop for. Emily Ellen was scampering through the field to pick it up. But July was laughing.

"Gosh," she said, "I had visions of Papa mixing my bread and doing my Saturday-night dishes. If I'd only seen them a little sooner, I'd have beaten you!"

"But you didn't," he crowed. "None of you can beat Old Man William. Not yet, by a long chalk. And what's more I can kick higher than any of you, too!"

He reached for July's ribbon, placed it atop the gatepost, and kicked. He kicked that ribbon right off the post, but his other leg came up, too, and he landed hard, the dust puffing out from under him as he hit.

Mama choked and the laughter pealed. Emily Ellen ran to him. "Are you hurt, Papa?" I think he was, but he waved away Tyler's outstretched hand, stood up slowly, and brushed the dust from his pants. Then, before limping to-ward the gate, he turned to us severely.

"And let that be a lesson to all of you. Pride goeth before a fall!"

That was the first of the annual block races which Papa was to win from each one of us in turn and lose five times, once to each of the boys. None of the girls ever won, and

ten years later I ran my last race, or rather walked it. He
wanted to be fair, he said, so he offered to do my dishes for
one week if I could beat him. Since he acknowledged that I
was a grown woman and we had more neighbors than we
had had before, and I was touchy about my dignity, I could
race him walking. If you think a running race is hard, go out
and try a fast walk. It was days before I got over my stiff-
ness and he quit teasing. I still had to do the dishes.

The times he lost, though, he was a good sport. "Well,
well," he'd say, "beat the old man! And I'm the one that's
proud. It'd be a sad son that couldn't outrace his Pa when he
was near a man grown!" And he did penance. Even during a
busy haying season when the watering turns were Tyler's
duty and they came at three o'clock in the morning, Papa
got up and watered. When Tyler protested that he would
not require the payment, Papa said: "A good man takes his
licking without complaining when he has earned one. I'll
water, boy."

By now there were twelve people living in our house.
Mostly we lived in the kitchen. It was a big kitchen and,
except for a washstand and a rocking chair, the rest of the
space was left for the table, with its stacks of extra leaves,
and the big black stove. That stove was another of my Job's
jobs. Mama blacked it and kept it shining. Tyler and Rollo
were detailed to keep the woodbox filled and empty the
ashes without dribbling, but it was my everlasting and un-
ending chore to keep its reservoir filled.

If you have never seen a reservoir, Allah be thanked, for
this is a gaping maw of iron that no self-respecting female
should know exists. On one side of the black stove was a
tank with a lid. It held water which heated whenever the
stove was fueled. The boys never seemed to mind filling the
woodbox, and that must have been an equally demanding

task, but I never heard them gripe about it. But then I didn't gripe either. At our house, you did what you were told. It had been known to happen that when you complained of being tired of one task, you were immediately relieved, but as the one given you to take its place was usually more distasteful, none of us complained much.

The woodcutting was the mad job. Whenever one of the boys was angry, he was set to chopping wood. I have seen Papa work off a lively anger on the woodpile and even Mama went out and hefted the ax, but with no great addition to the woodpile. We were, I insist, a very congenial and happy family, yet I can never remember a time when that woodpile was not at least half as high and half as long as the corral fence. Papa said: "A man without a temper is half a man, but a man who has a temper and cannot control it is no man at all!" The way he did it was apparently a man's own affair, but what do hot-tempered men do without a woodpile?

The Woodrow house was situated on the northwest corner of our lot. The rest of the block, except for the large house lot and its lawn and flowers, was taken up by a garden, corrals and barns, a granary, a pigpen (as far away from the house as possible), chicken coops, and a pasture with a deep hole in the middle of it. Whenever the boys were taking the watering turns, they channeled the water into the hole, and we went swimming. Papa kept his hayrack up on a wooden frame not far from the swimming hole, and he pastured horses there while he was breaking them to ride.

Aunt Molly Davis, Mama's widowed best friend, lived in the next block and we wore a path through the pasture, a shortcut to her house.

At night this walk, though a simple path in the daytime, could be a hazardous and fear-filled journey. Especially when your world was filled with the wee people that came from Grandma's stories and the other strange family ghosts we laughed at during the day and ran from at night. Mama had odd ways of punishment and I do not believe that she knew how terrible one of them was. An offender was often given the supper dishes to do. On a farm, milking the cows, feeding the animals, gathering eggs, and other daily chores are done after the day's regular work, and it is often late before supper is over. We usually ate about seven-thirty or eight o'clock so that Papa might sit at the head of the table.

Usually the supper dishes, the last duty of the day, was a rotating task for two, but if someone disobeyed, or was sassy or unfair or committed some such crime, the culprit was given the supper dishes to do alone, if it was Mama who meted our punishment. After the meal was over, she would gather up the rest of the family (Papa was out most evenings, ward teaching, visiting the sick, or on various marshal duties) and troop up to Aunt Molly's. At Aunt Molly's they popped corn or pulled candy or had a sing.

Down home, by the time all the dishes were washed and dried (the glassware had to sparkle), the reservoir filled, the kitchen floor swept, and the kitchen set to rights, the evening was over unless you hurried. I hurried.

Before I had the dishes washed, the empty house was usually filled with the wailing ghosts of the long dead, the thundering Prophet Isaiah, the outreaching arms of my little brother and sister who had died and who were lonesome up on cemetery hill, all the banshees of Ireland and the wee men of the Scots.

I would plan every move so that not one second was wasted. I filled the water bucket from the tap while I hurried to the table for dishes, unloaded the dishes, grabbed the bucket, dashed to the reservoir, emptied the water, and carried the bucket and more dishes on my return trip. I stacked the dishes so that a quick swipe with the towel would finish the drying, and as I shut the glass cupboard door with one hand, I opened the silverware drawer with the other.

When the work was done, I would run, pursued by grasping ghosts of all sizes and shapes, to arrive and sit on the step in the dark, listening to the laughter within, until I had caught my breath and could walk in calmly. I do not know how the others felt about that punishment, but for me, no whipping could have been worse. And my panic, one night, very nearly cost me my life.

For several days Papa had kept a young colt in the fenced pasture, barred at each end by poles, so that we usually bent and stepped through rather than slide them from their moorings. The gates were high enough so that the horses could not jump them. Mama had complained that the colt, a two-year-old, seemed very nervous.

"He rolled his eyes at me," she said. "And Dave, I'd rather you didn't keep him there. He seems sort of wild."

"I roll my eyes at you, too," he joked, "even if you are getting along in years." She swatted him and no one said any more about the colt. I'd stayed too late at school, playing, so I was doing dishes that night and Mama took everybody up to Aunt Molly's, as usual.

It was a summer evening and we'd had a cold early supper. There weren't many dishes and it was just darkening enough for the ghosts to start creeping out of their cracks when I gave the last swish to the dishpan and hung it on its nail in the pantry. Then I ran.

I slipped through the poles and started through the pasture. Suddenly, out of the dark came the ghost I'd dreaded all my life. It roared and thundered, towering above me, and it was real. The colt, evidently frightened by my running, had turned on me. I ran for the hayrack. Only a day or two before, Papa had finished with it and put it up on the frame. I ducked under and swung myself up through the wide, loose boards. The colt pawed and reared and hit the hayrack with his hooves. I screamed. I screamed as loud as I could, but no one heard me. Papa was not at home, the neighbor's lights were out across the street, and inside the warm safety of Aunt Molly's house, the family was making so much noise that they drowned out my screams. It got darker and I tried to slip from beneath the rack, but the horse heard me and came furiously back. I doubt very much if there is anything more terrifying than an angry horse.

I had snatched a couple of rocks and I threw them now as far as I could into the corner of the field. As the horse galloped toward the noise, I jumped down and ran to the nearest gate. The horse came after me. I could hear his snorting and the pounding of his hooves. He whinneyed in a high, insane way, and, rearing, came down on his sharp hooves just as I rolled in the dirt and gravel under the gate bars.

When I went in the house, Papa was home, the lamp was lit, and he was reading. I was scratched and bruised from the gravel and I was hysterical.

"The horse," I cried, "it was that damned horse." Papa overlooked my swearing as Mama most certainly would not have, even under the stress, and he went to the pasture. I don't know what he did with it, but the galloping ghost was not there the next morning and Papa gave me horehound sticks, enough to last a month, with rationing, even though I shared.

[CHAPTER EIGHT]

Wʜᴇɴ I ꜰɪʀꜱᴛ ʟᴇᴀʀɴᴇᴅ that the earth was constantly turning on its axle ("Axle, not axis—I'll bet you," Tyler argued, "like a wheel—it's got to be axle"), it was no surprise at all. This larger universe was only following the pattern of the Woodrow world. The big world, however, evidently did its own turning, which was concrete proof to me that God was a lot smarter than anyone I knew, even Papa. At our house things turned, but we turned them.

Before the town got together and built the creamery, Mama set the milk out in pans, and when the cream had come to the top, she skimmed it off and churned it into butter. The wooden churn was too big for us to hold in our laps and steady with our knees as Mama did. We had to put it on a chair. One of us would hold it down to keep it from slipping off while the other turned the handle. Sometimes, I never found the secret why, the butter would come with only a couple of hundred turns, but there were many mornings that we took turn and turn about before we would hear the welcome "clop" of the butter as it hit the paddles and the sides of the churn, and the loose swish of thinning buttermilk.

The reward for your work came when Mama scooped out the butter, worked it to squeeze out all the liquid, and pushed it into the pound butter mold. After she had pressed it solidly so that there would be no air pockets or short weight, she would ease it out of the wooden mold, pushing it firmly but gently, using the handle and the movable base of the mold skillfully. Suddenly, there you were, a whole twenty cents' worth of butter with four-leaf clovers imprinted on the top! One pound of butter could be traded to Mrs. Baum for four loaves of bread, if we had unexpected company and ran out.

The washing machine had to be turned, too. On washdays we took fifteen-minute turns and it was bend and raise, bend and raise, until your left arm felt ready to fall off, and then you turned around until the right one felt the same way. This was the waist-slimming exercise, and the Woodrow girls had the slimmest waists in town.

"Each struggle builds its own benefit," said Mama. She never ran out of them, neither struggles nor sayings.

Mama was proud of her washing. She made her own soap for it. More turning, just at a different angle—you stirred. We'd boil wood ashes in the "soap tub" until the yellow lye would come to the top, then Mama would skim this off. The lye, mixed with grease, carefully drained off and saved from cooking and rendered fat scraps, all of it strained and strained, was the base for the soap which we shredded for washday and used in bars for cleaning. Hand soap came from the store. It was pink, translucent, and fragrant. The bar was wrapped in paper that had a Japanese girl on the cover—Jap Rose. If you were so careless as to leave it in the bottom of the washbasin, or in the tub to soak into a gluey mass, woe be unto you. That was almost as sinful as forgetting it was Fast Sunday and nibbling.

Turning the washing machine wasn't the only work of washday. We had to turn the wringer handle, too. This exercise was designed to slim the throat and build the bust.

Washday started the night before. For a long time we did not have a water hydrant, so it was the twins' task to pull the brass boiler up two blocks to the Fisher's to fill it with water from their spring. Old Mr. and Mrs. Fisher always came out to the pumphouse to see June and July fill the boiler. The girls had to work fast to keep the water flowing. As they pumped, one on each end of the handle, their blond ringlets bounced, and the old people laughed and told Papa it was a bright spot in their week.

One of the few times I've known the twins to tattle was after a session with the wash-water pump. Hot and perspiring, they had pulled the wagon to the kitchen door and were about to look for Papa to lift the boiler in onto the stove, when Tyler, finding it convenient, relieved himself in it.

"Mama"—June's shock carried all the way out to the barn—"Mama, Tyler's peeing in the wash water!"

"Ah, it wasn't very much. Nobody would have known if she'd kept still." Tyler was not penitent. Aesthetically, clothes could not be washed in such defiled water, so Papa poured it out on the flowers and Tyler was made to refill the boiler, pumping every bit himself, while the twins watched in gleeful indignation. The day that Papa turned on the water hydrant just fifty feet from the kitchen was not only cause for celebration but cause for get-down-on-your-knees thankfulness.

The grindstone had to be turned, too. When Papa sharpened his scythe or his ax or whatever he was sharpening, and he sharpened a lot, we had to turn the handle to keep it going evenly as he dripped on the water to cool the stone and held the tool in place. If not our noses, we surely kept our hands to that grindstone for weary hours. Grinding evidently needed concentration, and Papa didn't sing or chat or tell you things when he sharpened. You just turned rhythmically and kept still.

Once I told Papa I thought the reason that the world shot stars and comets around so much was to break up the monotony of just turning and turning and turning. He said maybe I was right. No matter what you thought or how you felt, you couldn't surprise him much.

Mama was wonderful to surprise. She exclaimed and made a fuss and said she never dreamed you could do what you did, and you deserved a chalk mark on the wall. But as many times as she had said that, when Emily Ellen divided Papa's newly painted living-room wall into sections, one for each of us, and drew in the most recent marks of approval, she got spanked, hard. She'd used burnt wood charcoal on the wet paint.

Every time Mama went away, block teaching or to a funeral or to visit the sick, we surprised her. We did all the jobs we hated, like polishing the brass buckets and mixing bread and washing windows. We cleaned the silverware drawers and scrubbed behind the woodbox. We'd have supper ready, and Tyler, who liked to cook, would get it.

On these nights, we had dessert. Tyler would make his special bumfiddity fudge, and since he wouldn't reveal his recipe, we never found out what made it so terrible. Mama was always very pleased with us. She would sit in her rocking chair, without even unpinning her hat, and oh and ah, and simply wouldn't believe it. Every time!

On one of these "surprise days" we'd sent Rollo out with a bucket of water and two brooms. Aunt Molly's Ted, Rollo's daytime inseparable, needed a broom, too. Rollo was constantly untying apron strings, jumping out from behind doors, moving things we reached for. Scrubbing down the walks would keep him distant and useful. They scrubbed the walks and, when everyone was out of the kitchen, climbed up to the clock shelf where Papa kept the matches out of reach and went out and set the haystack on fire.

The fire was to have been only a little one, to be stomped out quickly if anyone came out the kitchen door. No one went outside and Papa arrived to find the boys frantically tossing dirt on a fire that was creeping up and over the haystack. Nothing could be done except watch and form a bucket brigade to keep the front of the barn wet. In the fall it would have been catastrophic. Now, in the spring, it only meant turning the cows out to graze a little earlier. Rollo and Ted were punished in keeping with their transgression. Papa let the cows come in the yard during the daytime to eat the grass and the boys had to keep them from eating the shrubs and to clean up after them at night until it was time to drive them back and forth to summer pasture. Taking the cows to pasture usually was a duty shared by us all. This summer, Rollo was sentenced to do it alone.

There was worse punishment than that, however. Emily Ellen's cat, Tatters, had moved her kittens into a pocket in the haystack and they were burned. She came to him with forgiveness and then she couldn't speak, and she sobbed and shook while he patted her and tried to give her his best flint.

Emily soon claimed another Tatters, for there were many cats living on the farm. Each of us had one or more. Papa was always loudly regretting that he hadn't drowned them before they opened their eyes, while all the time he was pouring out half a bucket of warm, foamy milk in their big milk pan. It made no difference how many we had; a new batch of baby kittens was an exciting event and we had contests to name them. An egg to sell at the store for penny candy was the usual prize.

Mama was always having contests, her enthusiastic name for work bees. One of them was the rug-sewing bee and this is the only time I tried to sew. We tore worn clothing or other materials—most anything would do, curtains, sheets, dyed underwear—into narrow strips and sewed the strips together for rag carpets.

We invited all our friends (who cordially invited us in turn), and Mama would serve lemonade and cookies. We sewed, and Mama wound the strips into huge balls to be made into carpets. If your strip broke three times while she was winding, you forfeited your chance at the prize, and the prizes were nice ones. Out of Mama's "new scrap" bag (she had an "old scrap" bag, too) came lovely things, a ruffled apron, a clothespin bag, a handkerchief folder, or sometimes a box (which originally had held chocolates) that she had padded and covered and divided into sections to hold needles and pins, doll clothes, or perhaps love letters. When I thought the prize was to be a "treasure box," I always stitched madly, but, as Mama frequently reminded us, practice makes perfect. This goes for sewing carpet rags, too, I guess. I was the only one who never sewed. I was the only one who never won a treasure box.

"Mama," July said, "there's something very wrong with all this."

"What's wrong?" Mama was always interested in straightening out kinks in us as well as in carpet rags.

"It's eternal, it goes on forever."

"We're very nearly through now. Another hour and we'll count balls to see who has won."

"Not just this, the whole thing. First you buy the material and make the clothes and wear them out and tear them up and wind them into balls. If it's something like this"—she held up one of Papa's shirts, which Tyler had worn, and Rollo after him—"you've spent, I bet, three months solid washing, hanging out, dampening down, and ironing. And I'm not counting the wood chopped, the fires built, the water carried. Then you cut, sew, and wind. Then you get it woven into a carpet like this one." She patted the floor with the toe of her slipper. "Then you tear holes in your hands and knees stretching it on Papa's carpet stretchers to get it on the floor, only to take it up every spring, sweep out the straw, haul in new straw, and kill yourself stretching it out straight again. By the time this carpet is worn out, I'll be an old woman, and think of all the work I'd have been saved if you'd never bought the material to make Papa that shirt in the first place!"

June invariably agreed. "She's so right, Mama. You're always telling us that like begets like, but in this family that should be changed to work begets work!"

"Well, get on with your begetting," Mama smiled. "It's nearly time to light the lamps, and Prilla"—she looked at me accusingly—"it was your turn to clean the chimneys this morning and they're still setting on the pantry shelf."

We had so much to be thankful for as we grew up! The water in the hydrant, the tap in the kitchen, the washer that didn't need turning, the creamery that bought our milk and sent us checks for it, along with the butter that we hadn't churned, and miraculous, oh, that wonderful Edison, I would have gladly kissed his shoes, when I watched Papa or Mama stretch to pull on the light cord. The light that didn't need its chimneys cleaned! There is no doubt in my mind that the secret of Thomas Alva Edison's long life was partly due to my grateful prayers that blessed him.

[CHAPTER NINE]

Our house did with wood and plaster what the loaves and fishes did for the multitudes. No matter how many people came, there was always room for them. We were grouped, I could never say divided, into two families, almost. There was the Before Mission Family and the After Mission Family. Emily Ellen was nearest to making a bridge between us.

Davy was running about, two and tousle-haired, almost able to carry on a conversation consisting of more than the subject and predicate, "I go," when Jeanne was born.

Jeanne was the last of the born children. "I'm made of odds and ends!" she was to complain bitterly. "Mama should have stopped at Davy. Looka here"—she showed the gaps in her mouth—"no-good teeth, and this"—she jerked at her spray-fine wisps—"leftover hair! It's a wonder you even had enough skin left to cover up my bones!"

But before Mama could chastise her for being ungrateful for the blessings of this earth, Marybeth's "Oh, but Jeanne, you've got dimples" comforted her.

"Pretty is as pretty does," Mama said sincerely. She said that to Jeanne more than to any of the rest of us, and Jeanne's desire to be pretty kept her on the road to righteousness far more successfully than any of the Ten Commandments could have done.

Jeanne was the practical one, always. Ingeniously practical. If one way wouldn't work to get a thing done, she could come up with a way that would. It was Jeanne who thought of using the snow shovels as sleds to slide down the sloping granary roofs, over piled-up snow at the bottom, and all the way across the winter-buried garden. It was Jeanne who made up the recipes for the endless cakes and mud pies she and Marybeth baked. It was Jeanne also who thought up the game of "Doses." This was one to test your fortitude. You filled a teaspoon with anything it would hold, eliminating known poisons, and your opponent swallowed your concoction while you, in turn, swallowed his. Generously I dosed Jeanne with a teaspoon of lard, plain. In turn I "opened my mouth and shut my eyes" to receive flour paste liberally sprinkled with kerosene and cayenne. That Jeanne was not to be trifled with was something I learned at a very early age, her early age.

The borrowed children kept coming. When Jeanne was slightly past a year, Mama's brother Jason's wife died a month after giving birth to Jeremy. Aunt Syble was another one of the Wyndham sisters. She not only looked like one of the painted elegances in the picture, she acted like one. Marybeth was three when Jeremy was born, and often I had heard Mama wail that "that child will never be able to lead a normal life." One visit to Aunt Syble's showed me why. The day we visited, Marybeth was dressed in ruffled and embroidered white. She sat quietly in the center of her mother's carefully made bed. Her little shoes were white kid and the soles were scarcely marred. She looked up at us sweetly with large, round, brown eyes. Black curls fell past her shoulders, caught back with tiny pearl barrettes and pink ribbons. She looked like something that Santa Claus might bring to a crown princess. Precisely, in a clear, small voice, she said "how do you do" and "thank you" and "please," and never asked to be taken off the bed. Indeed, if she had, I wondered if she would have been allowed. Things were to change.

Jeremy weighed ten pounds at birth, a broad-shouldered, black-haired, lusty youngster. I was to wonder later when Jeremy was being Jeremy if Aunt Syble had not chosen the simplest way after all. Her delicate sensitivity could never have borne his growing up. He was meant to be a member of a big family. A small one couldn't have survived him.

The night Jeremy and Marybeth came was a sad one. Uncle Jason brought them in, bundled in shawls, Marybeth under one arm and Jeremy cradled in the other. It was snowing hard outside and we heard the heavy crunch of his feet on the snow even before the door burst open. Suddenly our quiet kitchen was full and noisy. The lamp was lit in the center of the kitchen table, for we had been studying. The four smallest were tucked into bed. Emily Ellen was patiently holding her hands for Mama's unwinding yarn, and Papa was reading. Occasionally, he would interrupt our studying to read and interpret a passage. "It's a wonder how people can say the Bible is hard to understand," he would exclaim wonderingly. "Why, it's as clear as a bell, Kate, as clear as a bell. Truly a marvel to behold!"

Mama dropped her yarn. Papa closed the Bible, being careful to insert its narrow, black silk-ribbon marker into his place, and stood up. Mama reached for the baby, who started to squall as she unwrapped him.

"I brought them to you, Kate. I know you and Dave will treat them like your own."

"And isn't this a fine girl?" Papa was reaching behind Uncle Jason's knees to draw the still swaddled Marybeth to him. "Take off her bonnet, Prilla. See those black eyes. Ah, she's a rare little beauty!" But Marybeth was not happy. I tried to take off her bonnet, but she clutched it, crushing it down on her head, and when I unbuttoned her red-velvet coat, she buttoned it up again quickly.

"I do not want to stay here," she said. "I want to go home." It was then that Mama cried, and I knew why, for this petted little one who could not again be the center of anyone's world for a long time to come. I sensed her disdain for all of these people, her wanting to go home to her scrubbed toys and her meticulous life, and my heart ached for her. It was June, though, who walked over and picked her up.

"You'll like it here," she promised sincerely. "We have a lot of fun at our house. There's someone to play with all the time. No one ever gets lonely." ("And no one ever has any privacy," I muttered. June threw me a disapproving glance.) "We sing songs and we make taffy at night and we don't have any three-year-old little girls. We've been saving that place just for you." Marybeth took the place we'd saved for her. Not so Jeremy. He went on protesting loudly for days.

Uncle Jason had been called on a Mission to New Zealand, no doubt to salve his soul for his recent loss. He was never really going to return. Oh, he came back from his Mission, which was longer than Papa's. I think it was extended a while. He was gone a little over four years. He came back with bags of wonderful smooth shells and carved wooden idols and woven mat rugs in indescribably pagan patterns. They were slick when you put them on the floor and would never stay unrolled at the edges, for they had remained rolled tightly for too many months on their way here.

Perhaps Uncle Jason was rolled up too tightly, too, for he never unrolled completely either, and though his children adored him always, he saw little of them. Jeremy was our boy and Marybeth was our sister just as surely as if their name had been Woodrow and not Campbell.

When Uncle Jason brought them in, I wondered where we were going to put them, but Mama did not seem troubled. She moved Jeanne from the place on her arm in the big featherbed that she and Papa shared and tucked her, still sleeping, at its foot. Jeremy was the baby now.

Jeanne accepted the change without a murmur. For that night, June took Marybeth into their bed and she and July told her stories until she fell contentedly asleep. After that she replaced Davy in his trundle and he moved to a cot (with a mattress which Mama stitched up rapidly out of ticking and filled with straw) in the room with the three other boys, Tyler, Rollo, and Boot. Grandma still lived and slept in wondrous aloneness in the living room. June, July, Frances, Emily Ellen, and I shared the other bedroom with its two big beds. Mama and Papa were crowded, for their bedroom, large as it was, was not large enough for two babies and a trundle.

As the old history books say, the ones written by people who lived here in the valleys of the mountains: "It was a trying time for the Saints." It was at this time that Papa withdrew his meager savings from the bank and built the little room—the little room that was hardly big enough for one bed, a chest of drawers, and a night table. For a while he and Mama slept here while they turned their spacious bedroom over to the babies and the milk safe. When they moved back, the boys' bedroom became the parlor, and the little room was eventually all mine, alone, by myself, my escape. For me it would be big enough, and it was private.

When we had company, we moved the babies' beds into the two big bedrooms and set Grandma's next-best bedstead up along with sundry cots and floor beds. Only company took precedence over Grandma. When Aunt Sally and her plump and laughing youngsters came, the overflow had to move into the living room. Then we unfolded Grandma's vast, ornate folding bed and here was room for more. This bed, unused, was a storage place for the stacks of hand-pieced quilts that we all worked on during the winters and in any speck of spare time we had after we were big enough to see over the quilting frames.

Nearly always, Grandma had the quilting frames set up in the middle of her room. As we worked, we rolled the quilt and its neatly stitched, elaborate patterns underneath the frames, and as the roll around the frames grew thicker there was less and less to do. Papa quilted, to show us that he could do anything as well as we could. Rollo quilted because he liked us and liked to be with us. Even Tyler, tall and stooped and silent, would sometimes grin and thread a needle expertly. "I'd like to see this damn thing out of the way for a while" was his excuse.

Our "two families" were remarkably congenial, I thought. I didn't mind ironing for the little ones, and until she grew out of them, I loved doing Marybeth's fussy, embroidered dimities and lace-trimmed lawn dresses. She seemed a little out of place with us. Jeremy's hair faded to a warm brown, not too far off from Emily Ellen's burnished auburn, but Marybeth was a pheasant in a henyard. She had the loveliest sheeny black hair I've ever seen, and Mama thought so, too. It was really quite a chore to do it up, although it curled naturally, which helped, but Mama patiently brushed and ringleted and then just as patiently brushed and tried to ringlet Jeanne's thin, fine blond locks.

The first Sunday dress Mama made for Marybeth was a comedown. "Mama Kate," she protested, "this is not a Sunday dress. This is an everyday go-downtown-or-visit-the neighbors dress." And indeed it was. There was no fancy tucking, no expensive lace, no delicate pleats or silk sash. It was plaid and nicely made. Plain, except for its white collar and cuffs, it had pleats, but there were only two, front and back, and the bodice was set in with a tiny trim of white. For us it was a very nice Sunday dress, but Marybeth's chin shook, and it was June, again, who tactfully explained, while she slipped it over Marybeth's head.

"You see, honey, all your other pretty dresses are too small. We've let them down all we can. Besides they are baby dresses. You're just growing up so fast that you will have to wear grown-up-lady Sunday dresses, like the big girls do. And, you know, Mama is making July and me a dress out of this very material and we'll have her make it just like this and wear it to church with you so we'll be triplets!" That was all it took, for, young as she was, Marybeth sensed the special sort of fun that June and July had together.

Jeanne had been standing by, listening. When Mama, with Marybeth's consent, wanted Jeanne to wear the re-hemmed, still-pretty little dresses, Jeanne refused.

"I not," she said positively, "a itto baby. I big. Put 'em on Jeremy." At that Marybeth rebelled, for she was not fond of Jeremy, who took everyone's time and who squalled so loudly. "No," she said, "Jeremy cannot. I'll save them for my little girl." She packed them into a small flower-topped metal trunk that had been her mother's and was now her "own thing" in a house that was full of shared things, and I never saw them again.

Jeremy had been born a sturdy, healthy baby, but we came near to losing him. Shortly after Uncle Jason had left to forget, Jeremy developed some sort of gland trouble. His little neck would swell until he looked like Rollo did when he had the mumps. He had to be held upright in order to breathe, and we took turns. Grandma and Mama spelled off during the day and when we came home from school we held him. His high wails, half distressed kitten, half hallo-ween noisemaker, were almost constant. He wriggled and he twisted. Between the crying and the gasping for breath, his small face would redden and he was, to say the least, not a pretty baby. Papa would hold him at night when he came in from the fields, and many times I waked to his whimpering and heard Tyler's deepening voice or Rollo's chuckling one trying to soothe him into slumber. I was often shaken out of sleep to stagger through the cold house, trying to step on the braided rugs to keep my feet from the shock of the sub-zero linoleum, to take my turn with Jeremy.

Sitting in the darkness of the living room, I would listen to Grandma's contented snoring and watch the flames from the hingeholes of the potbellied stove flicker on the ceiling while I held Jeremy upright until my arms ached with weariness.

Once I rebelled and dumped him on the couch to scream it out, but he choked up and fought for breath and I grabbed him back up and held him against my shoulder and finally heard him breathe easily again.

"Oh, thank You, thank You," I prayed, and I was much gentler with him after that. He was so little and sick and helpless.

Finally, his baby plumpness was gone and he gasped noisily for breath. We thought we were surely going to have to write Uncle Jason that the little son had followed his mother home.

"Faith and prayers," said Mama, "are priceless, but the Lord expects us to use common sense, too." She coerced the doctor into lancing the bulbous swellings, and after two terrible days and nights, they slowly drained and healed, leaving inch-long welts to embarrass him later when the girls, using any excuse to talk to him, teased him about the scars. But in those months when Jeanne was pushed abruptly out of her babyhood and Jeremy took her place, he fused himself into the family. He was always in trouble, one way or another, but it was "Jeremy" trouble that, although almost impossible to live with, brought more laughter than tears when it was over.

Papa thanked the Lord gratefully for all His blessings in restoring Jeremy to health and for the little souls they were privileged to care for.

"They should have been grateful for twins," said June

after Papa's prayers that night when we were getting into bed. "You know darn well who washes all the diapers around here. Mama says there is nothing better to make your hands pretty than washing diapers. And if that's true, July and I would win the Beautiful Hands Contest hands down, or up."

I remember Mama praying that the house would never be without a baby, and thought that, one way or another, the Lord was answering her prayers. Generously! I knew, too, if Mama didn't, why Aunt Marthe had "aye'd" when she heard her, for though these little ones were huggable and affectionate, it meant more clothes to wash, more dishes to do, more hours to spend finding things to amuse them when you were dying to get to the end of the chapter.

Mama looked at me in shock one day when I said: "I'm going to limit my family to two or three children. They're too much work."

"Prilla Lou Woodrow, you don't know the meaning of work and you don't know the meaning of blessings, either. Go get some chips to start this fire! Right now!"

Mama was right. If I wondered how she could be so generous with her desserts and her Christmas treats, it never entered my mind to wonder how many pairs of shoes, or dresses, or pretty bits of jewelry (which she so loved when we grew older and gifted her with them) she went without equally for her owned and her borrowed children.

Jeanne didn't seem to mind that another baby had taken her place. She made Jeremy her special charge, ran on her short legs to get his diapers, his bottle, and to pick up the spools he threw on the floor. She said he was her "doll boy."

After the operation on his throat, Jeremy thrived. He

slept well and ate enormously, something he never stopped doing, it seemed to me. He clung to the comfort of his bottle and at two years old still insisted on milk in the night despite all efforts to wean him. Teasing and threats got us nowhere. He would have that bottle or he would scream. He got the bottle. It was Jeanne who would spat in her bare feet and long flannel nightgown to the milk safe and fill up the bottle. She would carefully skim back the thick cream from a round pan and with a little funnel and cup pour the milk into his green-glass bottle and flip the nipple on it expertly. It was Jeanne who convinced him to give it up. She got his bottle and the turpentine bottle mixed.

She had padded sleepily into the pantry to get his bottle and by mistake took the one that Papa had left on the table. She filled it up with milk and took it back to Jeremy. One choking swallow and he slammed the bottle away. Then Mama worried for a year because she couldn't get him to drink milk at all. He got over that, too. I've seen him sit down and empty the contents of a two-quart pitcher, and when we murmured, amazed, Mama would put a hand on his shoulder.

"Now that will be enough from you. Growing boys need lots of nourishment. And Jeremy is going to be a big man."

"Especially around," I said, but Mama thimble-pied me smartly on the back of my head. And I bowed to her greater tolerance.

Jeanne demanded a stiff price for taking care of Jeremy. If she needed a small puppy in her games, he was the puppy. If she wanted him to be a crying baby in a ruffled bonnet, he was the baby, and she extracted instant obedience from him. When he was nearly four and an inch taller than she was, he, more and more often, would defy her. It was then that she and Marybeth began the "reign of terror."

The little girls were very domestic. They sewed, they baked cakes, they made pies. Their baked goods were exact duplicates of Mama's except that they used a very choice grade of dirt for flour. It was Jeremy's duty as the husband to eat their lovely food and pat his stomach in praise, as Papa always did.

When confronted with a fresh array of pastry warm from their sun oven, one afternoon, Jeremy rebelled. He could see that his rebellion was going to be physically put down, so he scrambled up into an apple tree which shaded the grassy patch they called their house. He knew the girls would not follow him—they might tear their dresses—and he thought he was safe. He underestimated them. Marybeth got the rake and Jeanne ran to the barn for a pitchfork, and they jabbed him out of the tree. He broke his arm, a compound fracture—the jagged bone fragment protruded through the skin. They were frightened at what they had done, but not too frightened to be practical. Jeanne scampered after Mama while Marybeth carefully spread her skirt and, avoiding the bleeding arm, brushed the leaves from Jeremy's head and placed it in her lap. Leaning over him, she warned: "If you dare tell Mama Kate what we did, I'll break your other arm!"

I glanced through the pantry window just as he fell from the tree, but though I ran to his aid, I knew better than to interfere in their domestic relations if I didn't want Mama to know that I rolled my underwear up above my knees and put beet juice on my lips after I left for school in the mornings. Jeremy told me later what Marybeth had whispered, and he knew as I did that she meant every word.

Spring housecleaning was a horror I began worrying about immediately after the Christmas holidays. As I've already said, Mama belonged to the "take everything out, down, off, or up" school of housecleaning. We had reached the rug-removal stage in the living room when Marybeth discovered the trap door in the floor which led down to the spiderwebby cellar. Thinking as one, she and Jeanne removed the door, covered the hole with a long rag rug, and diabolically called Jeremy for a game of tag. Their steps echoed on the floor and they ran clattering around the room, from which all the furniture had been removed except the oak table in the center. The girls ran in this corner and that, Jeremy trying to catch them. Around the table they ran, leaping over the covered trap. The first time round, Jeremy miraculously avoided the rug; the second time, down he went!

Marybeth ran sobbing tearlessly to Mama and we looked down to see Jeremy supine and relaxed, unconscious on the hard dirt of the cellar floor.

"What were you trying to do?" I asked them as I brushed their hair and rolled it into rag curls for church the next morning. "Kill him?"

"Course not," Jeanne said, "it was only a little way down. At the most it would have only broke his other arm."

[CHAPTER TEN]

ALTHOUGH THE MISSION certainly strengthened our charac-
ters, and after it is over a character-strengthening experience
can be valuable, while you are in the midst of one, you
usually wish you were somewhere else. We watched our
friends get bicycles and new dresses, and though we were
proud to be "serving the Lord in our humble way," it was
not without slipping a wee bit off the straight and narrow.
We coveted quite frequently.

It was worse after Papa came home. Although Mama had
done an inspired job of keeping out of debt, neither Papa
nor Mama was inclined to pour out good money on folde-
rols when we needed a new room on the house, the fields
had to be planted, Papa wanted to add to his herd, and he

had to buy a new wagon. It was necessary for Papa to dress neatly, too. His position as town marshal and his ready tongue made him in demand at funerals, golden weddings, reunions, and on all occasions calling for "Dear friends,, now we are gathered together . . ." Until they had bought the necessities and had a little money in the bank to fall back on, we made do or went without.

Emily Ellen was growing into a beautiful girl and a loving and giving one, but even she had her bone of contention.

"Mama," she complained bitterly one morning. "If you knew how I want to throw up every time I have to put on one of these hand-me-down dresses. By the time Prilla gets through with them, even though they were pretty when you made them for June and July, they're not pretty any more. Look here." With a gentle pull she ripped the worn sleeve of the one she held. "You hem them up again for me and I feel funny." Mama was opening her mouth to say something about false pride, but I knew how Emily Ellen felt.

"She's right, Mama. It's getting so the folks in town can recognize us as the Woodrow girls right easily. They know the dress, they just don't know which one of us is wearing it!"

So, Mama, resourceful as ever, kept on giving me June and July's outgrown things, but only every other discard now. The others she would make over for Emily. Taking two dresses of the twins and cutting and matching, Emily usually had a different style of dress, but at a distance, she remarked resignedly, anyone would still know it was one of us from the dress goods.

We worked and pooled our money and Papa gradually

got caught up. He built the north porch, painted the house, and bought two new milk cows.

For Emily Ellen's birthday each of us contributed a little money and Mama bought a piece of white faille. She made it up into a sort of a jumper with set-in sleeves of pink flowered silk and a set-in bodice of the same material. Emily treasured that dress. I found her in the closet a couple of times pressing a fold of it against her cheek and crooning to it as she did to the baby kittens.

But this was during the ascendancy of the Terrors, and Emily Ellen, like the rest of us, didn't escape. One Saturday afternoon we'd been practicing a musical number that we were to do in church the next evening, and Emily was visiting somewhere. Marybeth and Jeanne had been wonderfully quiet and Jeremy was sleeping the afternoon away in the coolness of Mama's bedroom.

We heard the gate squeak, the kitchen door explode and shut, and then a high scream of pain from Emily Ellen.

In the kitchen, behind the stove, sitting in the woodbox, were the two little girls. They were being dressmakers. For their dolls' Sunday dresses, they had snipped the sleeves from Emily Ellen's new dress and were slicing jaggedly down the front to get a nice piece of material for the coats.

We had to forcibly restrain Emily. She was going to use the stove poker on them. Mama tanned their legs with a willow, chasing them from out the Magic Circle, where they had run for King's X. They wept and were sorry, but Emily Ellen was bitterly unforgiving. She never did forgive them for it and never spoke to them on the days she had to wear the dress, carefully pieced together by Mama. Even Mama's tiny desperate stitches and a winding appliqué of bias tape could not camouflage the damage.

None of us was to escape the Terrible Trio. When the twins entertained their callers in the front room, they did so with trepidation. Even when they stationed themselves stiffly to watch all of the three entrances into the room, Jeremy might creep from behind the folding bed to jab a hatpin up through the chair bottom where Clay Winston, June's favorite beau, sat. Or worse, infinitely worse, he'd come in and ask for aid to go to the toilet. "I can't get my pants undone," he'd state mournfully. "You'll be sorry if you don't come quick!" I still say that it was Clay's matter-of-fact offers to help and his quick removal of Jeremy from the room that were the deciding factors when June made her choice. For a boy without any little brothers and sisters, he had remarkable aplomb.

With so many of us going in and out and hither and yon, it was almost inevitable, according to the law of averages, that one of us was doing something that he shouldn't be. All of Papa and Mama's oft-expressed desire to see the faces of their family gathered around them was not due, I am sure, to parental fondness. Some of that desire was a result of just plain wanting to keep an eye on us.

In any given year the number of broken dishes far exceeded the number of people who admitted breaking them. None of us knew how our clothes got torn, how expectant cats found such nice comfortable beds to have their kittens in, or who carved everyone's initials into the baby squash? Every year Papa warned us that though it was mighty interesting to see names half an inch high stretch to six or seven inches or more, the carving made the squash subject to easy spoiling. Those squash, like Eve's apple, were beyond human strength to resist. I only carved once, but once multiplied by all of us amounted to years of carved squash.

As I have said before if you merited punishment, it came swiftly, and all of us knew this well. Still, we kept on doing things that would bring retribution down upon our heads, sometimes in the form of Papa's big hand or in other more lasting ways.

For a year or so all of us had been pleading for a bike. The paper route would be easier for June. Rollo's deliveries could be made in half the time or less. We'd be willing to sign up for it in turn for work and pleasure, and we could get along sharing just one. We almost got one, too. If it hadn't been for July and Tyler.

Mama still sewed to help out and occasionally she derived real pleasure from her work. She loved making wedding dresses, and when she was in the middle of a wedding, none of us were allowed to track into the living room, where she set up the machine. She was working on one now, for Aunt Lizzie Adair's daughter, and she ran out of thread.

"Hurry," she told July, "hurry downtown and get me a spool of white number sixty. While you're down there, get me three yards of pillow ticking. I'm going to give Dorothy Adair a pair of pillows for her wedding present. I've got the feathers all washed and dried. Now hurry, mind you. This dress must be finished by tomorrow night."

July asked Tyler to go along for company and, as he was in one of his rare moments of leisure, he jumped the fence and walked with her. Somehow, somewhere, on that walk Satan got in front of them. They took the money for the thread and the pillow ticking, rented a bike from George Jasperson for five cents, and rode, taking turns pumping one another, all the way to Midway and Luke's Hot Pots. To this day I can't think where they got so much brazen courage. It must have been Satan. They stayed all day, swimming and buying themselves a barbecue sandwich.

Mama, meantime, was as furious as I have ever seen her. She could go no further on the dress without thread. White number forty the neighbors had, but it was too coarse to use on the dress. She would have sent one of us to get another spool but she had no more money. She thought for a little while that they had met with an accident, but in our town news of an accident would have come within an hour.

"Those children are spreeing!" she said. "I just know it. They've either spent the money and are hid up somewhere, or they've lost it and don't dare to come home." She was pacing the yard, her blue skirts switching behind her as she walked, her narrow hands jerking her apron this way and that. I was a little bit, more than a little bit, afraid of her.

Frances spied them first. She had run over to the corner for the fourth or fifth time, at Mama's bidding, to see if they were coming. "Here they come, Mama Kate, and they aren't limping. They're all right."

When July and Tyler confessed, Mama was speechless. "Go to your rooms," she said. "If I punished you now, your Papa would have to jail me for murder. Right this minute, I can't stand to see the face of either of you!" She was sitting on the porch, crying with vexation, when Papa came home with a load of flour from the mill. Lying on top of the load was a bright red bicycle. He'd traded Ole Olson three young pigs for it, at a considerable sacrifice.

"Papa's brought us a bike. Papa's brought us a bike," yelled Boot, and we all ran to be the first to see it when he lifted it down, but Mama was there first.

"You'll take it back, Dave." she said. July and Tyler heard her, for they had come from their rooms at our excited squeals.

Papa paused in lifting it down.

"Now, what's all this?"

Mama told him about the dress unsewed on her table, the money spent, the two lost souls in exile, and Papa unloaded the flour, put the bike in the wagon bed, and drove back to the miller's with it. We all cried, copiously and noisily. But Mama refused to have the bike on the premises and Papa agreed that the punishment was merited.

"Why should all of us be punished, too? Couldn't you just not let July and Tyler ride it?" I asked.

"How long do you think you'd enjoy it if they couldn't?" Mama pointed out. She was right, but when I think of it now, I can feel the tears of disappointment gather behind my lids.

Papa saddled the horse and rode downtown to get Mama's thread. She stayed up all night to finish the dress in time. We used the money Ole gave Papa, in lieu of the bike, for a wedding present for Dorothy, and July and Tyler trod the straight and narrow carefully for quite some time.

"It will teach all of you a lesson," said Mama. "The innocent are always caught up in the punishment of the guilty." And, a little unreasonably I thought, she added: "you'd better watch the company you keep!"

"You mean," I asked, "you don't want us to have anything to do with July and Tyler any more?"

"Of course not!" she snapped. "Just don't keep company with people like them!"

The worst thing about crime is that it can start so innocently. Sometimes just in doing a good deed for somebody else we found ourselves all tangled up in a maze of sin and retribution that left us helpless when Papa or Mama said: "Explain yourself. Just give me an unvarnished reasonable explanation of why." It was easier to be punished than to be unvarnished and reasonable.

Papa had warned all of us that we were not to take Diamond out unless we allowed her new colt to go along. But half the fun of driving Diamond was that she was so fast, and the colt couldn't run very fast or very far. One time Mama had been regretting that she just couldn't get away to gather chokecherries for her favorite jelly and so June and July decided to go get them for her as a surprise. They took Ted Davis's older sister, Leone, to help with the picking. With the three of them it wouldn't take long.

A trip halfway down Provo Canyon was too much for the colt. Besides it wouldn't hurt him to stay in the nice, cool barn on such a hot day. They left him there and didn't have any trouble until they'd nearly finished filling their pails.

Then Leone saw the bear. It might have been a cub, but to hear them, no Kodiak could be bigger. They left their buckets and berries and ran for the buggy. They managed to scramble in, but Diamond had sensed their fright, and off she went. They couldn't hold her, and the corral gate didn't stop her either. She ran right through that, buggy and all. Only the hungry whinny of her colt slowed her down, but by then she was so excited trying to get in to him that the twins couldn't even unhitch the buggy. She very nearly smashed it to bits before Papa came running out of the house.

They were trying to get the barn door open to let the colt out so that Diamond would calm down, but Papa got there in time to stop them. That's the only time I've ever known him to get mad enough to swing his heavy hand at them. He whapped them both good, big girls that they were, and swore, which astonished them mightily.

"Damn it to hell!" he raged. "A man can't keep a damn thing around this place. Get in the house. *Get in the house!*"

The twins got, and Leone ran home and didn't dare show her face for a week. If Papa hadn't been there, the colt would have been let out to nurse and, with Diamond all hot from running, probably would have died from colic.

This time Papa was in no mood to listen to an unvarnished reasonable explanation. (Mama tried to put in a word for their thought for her chokecherries.) When they tearfully tried it, he looked over his paper in furious disgust and said, to put all of us in a state of shock for days: "Dry up, the lot of you. Another word out of any one of you and I'll be tempted to knock her block off." Our tender, loving Papa!

The only time I've seen him as disgusted was when Tyler and Rollo, after reading about how Leonardo da Vinci had failed in his experiment with wings, thought they wouldn't. They built a fragile contraption in secret in the hayloft, assembled it on a Sunday when Papa was to be in Charleston preaching at Ward Conference, and launched it off the barn roof. Their experiment repeated da Vinci's and they not only broke the Sabbath but broke a leg each. Rollo's left, Tyler's right.

"It's too bad one of you couldn't have broken both legs," Papa said without sympathy. "I'd have had one hay hand this summer at least." But the rest of us were more sympathetic, even if it meant that we had to work as hay hands until the boys were up and around again. They were appreciative, though. They did the dishes, helped with the ironing, and watched the little kids as soon as they could get out of bed, and Papa didn't allow them any dallying. Actually, I don't think either of them minded the switch in chores until old Lizzie Jones came to call on Mama one afternoon and then it was all over town about the Woodrow boys wearing aprons.

The only time I have seen Papa as mad as he was about the chokecherry trip was when Ralph Jones gifted him with a racing buggy. Ralph had been sweet on June for a long time, but neither Papa nor Mama took to him. I thought he was nice enough. He never came to see June without a sack of chocolates. She saw to it he didn't eat any of them, so that there'd be at least one around for the rest of us.

June never seemed to get very excited about his coming, and this only made him come oftener. He had a very nice singing voice, though, and when June and July and Tyler and Ralph sang, even Papa sneaked up on the north porch so he could listen. They sang all the popular songs, "I Want a Girl, Just Like the Girl," "Drifting and Dreaming," "When You and I Were Seventeen."

Ralph could see, along with the rest of us, that he wasn't making the grade with June, or with Papa. To impress her and win Papa's support, he brought over from Park City, where he lived, a brand-spanking-new racing buggy.

"It's a gift, Mr. Woodrow. My father took it in on an account, and he let me have it cheap. Real cheap! Nobody in the county can put it to as good a use as you can with that trotting horse of yours. I just wanted to give it to you, that's all." His pleasure in giving was so evident, and where Diamond was concerned Papa's resistance was low. He accepted it and, acting no older than his sons, he couldn't wait to try it out. The buggy was a smashing success. Every time Papa thought of Ralph's sort of washed-out eyes and not too broad shoulders, he'd think of the gleam of that buggy and said: "Well, maybe I ought not to be so hard on the boy!"

Then one afternoon he came back from a run with Diamond to find two lawmen from Park City waiting on the porch for him. They were there to reclaim stolen property.

"Stolen property? You'll find no stolen property on this place. I'll guarantee you that." In indignation, Papa was about to throw his brother officers off the lot.

"We found it. You just drove up in it."

Ralph had stolen the buggy from the livery stable in Park City. How he thought he could get away with it, I'll never know. The same way that Rollo thought he'd get away with building a small fire in the hay, or Tyler and July with their trip to Midway on Mama's thread money, I guess.

"If I ever," Papa warned June, "find that boy on this place again I will kick his rear end so hard he'll find his legs where his arms should be!"

"But, Papa," I said, trying to defend poor Ralph, "he did it for love, and you always say a man will do anything for the woman he loves, even crawl on . . ."

"And that, Critic, will be enough out of you."

"But what if June loves him?"

"Then she'll have to find a new beau!" Papa said crossly. "Love is like a bee. It can light on a rose as well as a cow turd!"

It was Mama that came up with the maxims; Papa usually quoted from the Bible, but I guess he couldn't remember anything apt. "A gift is as a precious stone in the eyes of him that hath it; whithersoever it turneth it prospereth" didn't quite fit the situation.

[CHAPTER ELEVEN]

GROWING UP seems to take such a long time, yet growing old takes such a short while. Papa's Mission had made us grow up faster than we would have, Tyler especially, I think. Being the man of the house during those years forced him into maturity. When Papa came home it was almost immediately evident that Tyler resented Papa and his kindly, though oftentimes heavy-handed authority. Rollo went his merry way, and though sometimes he did unacceptable things, they seldom brought on Papa's wrath. There was a sort of man-to-boy understanding between them. "Just gimme time, Pa. I'll grow up." And Papa smilingly agreed that he would.

With Tyler it was different. His resentment toward Papa

grew very quietly, and after the chores were done one Sunday morning Tyler went away. He packed his clothes in a gunnysack and climbed unseen aboard the "Creeper." From Provo he went to Ogden and then, lashing himself with his belt to the top of a boxcar, he rode through the heat and wind until he slipped off the train at a water tower in Nevada and hiked up to the sprawling farm buildings he could see from the stop. He said he was a good hand, and a ranch, in the midst of haying, could always use a good hand.

He had left a note for Mama and I read it to her. Always I was the one to read the letters and the notes and the telegrams when they came. She wept when I read it, and I felt her heartbreak, but I could not condemn Tyler, for I had seen him, always serious, becoming more and more indrawn. I'd try to talk to him, but he'd only grin at me with his eyes dark and unsmiling and say in his husky, drawling way: "Go on, Miss Nosy, you don't have to know what everybody thinks."

The note said briefly: "I'm tired of being just the oldest boy. I want to be myself, so I'm going away to do it. Don't worry, Mama, I can take care of myself. Tell Papa he needs to get a new pair of hobbles for Old Bell. Someday she's going to bust loose and send one of the kids sailing. Love. Tyler."

Tyler didn't write again and we knew nothing of him until the morning of Mama's dream. Papa missed him a lot, I know. I heard him telling Mama that maybe he had been too strict with Tyler, maybe asked too much of him. But who could a man ask a lot of if it wasn't his own sons? Then he said: "But if that's what the boy wants, the Lord bless him. He's got a home to come to any time he needs it." I thought it was too bad he had never said that to Tyler.

With Tyler gone, Boot drove the hayrack and Rollo and Papa pitched the hay on the load. The twins and I took turns going to the field to tromp hay and staying home to help Mama with the babies and the housework. I hated to tromp the hay in the heat. My legs, though I wore a pair of Rollo's pants tightly tied around the ankles, would itch. I got sunburned and twig-scratched, and a couple of times irate honey bees attacked me.

Hauling the hay from the south field was a loathsome task, but when we hauled it from the north field, the ride home on top of that towering load was almost worth all the work. It was about ten miles from the house to the field and back and two loads a day were all that we could bring in even though we started as soon as it was light. On the way out, I was embarrassed riding through the center of town dressed like a boy with my hair tucked under Tyler's old straw hat. The first trip wasn't so bad, because nobody was up except other hay haulers, or the doctor out on an early sick call, but the second time, just after lunch, was horrible. It seemed like all my friends were out shopping, and the time I saw Tom Collins sitting in his dad's surrey (I was sort of sweet on Tom) nearly did me in. I refused to haul hay for two days after that, but it was even worse for June and July. They had always been more dignified than I was, and I felt sorrier for them than I did for myself, and there wasn't any use for all of us to get brown as Indians. There should be a couple of ladies in the family. So I finished the summer.

The ride home, though, was wonderful. I'd lie on my back and watch the clouds and hear the clop of the horses' hooves. Buried unseen in the middle of the load, I'd smell the sweetness of that new hay and suck on a hard candy that Mama usually tucked in our pockets when we had something unpleasant to do. "To sweeten the sour," she said. I could tell just about where we were from the direction we were going, though I could only see the tops of the cotton-wood trees and the blue sky above. I was always saddened when we turned in the barnyard gate. The lovely ride was over.

We'd unload the hay with a hayfork, which was sus-pended on ropes from three high poles, spearing huge chunks from the hayrack. We used a rope pulley attached to a singletree to which the horse was harnessed. It was my job to straddle that wide-backed old work horse and "get up and whoa" him back and forth down the narrow aisle between the barn and the ascending haystack. As he strained forward slowly, the hayfork was pulled by a guide rope over the hay, and when the fork was in position, Papa would trip the rope and the hay would fall onto the stack. Then he and Rollo would neatly and quickly stack the hay so the haystack re-mained squared off until the final loads, when they rounded it at the top.

Relieved of his load, Old Dick would back reluctantly, lowering the hayfork so that Rollo could clamp its teeth into another mouthful of hay from the hayrack.

More often than not throughout the long, hot summer, July would be waiting at the gate. Covered from throat to ankle against the sun, she'd ride the sweaty old horse while I went in out of the sun, usually to fill the reservoir again. "A change is as good as a rest." Mama, again.

One late afternoon, the last load of the season on the rack, July walked down a block to meet us and ride in on top of the load. Papa thought that she was firmly atop the hay and started up the horses. The hay was heavy and the horses started with a jerk to get the rack moving. In that moment between the quick jerk and the rolling of the wheels, July was jarred from the top and, grasping desperately for handholds, she slipped down underneath the rack. The iron-rimmed back wheel rolled diagonally across her waist and stomach. I screamed for Papa to stop as she slipped, but he thought we were just fooling. Rollo yelled and grabbed for the reins. Papa, seeing his face, stopped the team.

July was lying in the dust of the road, very still. We all ran to her and then Rollo sprinted for home and Mama. I was relieved that she didn't seem to be bleeding anywhere, but as we knelt there by her she started to gasp, jerking painfully.

Across the road, the water ran icy cold in the wide, shallow ditch. Papa picked July up in his arms and carried her over to it. Then he lowered her down into the water. I don't know why he did this; I guess because it was the only thing he could think to do. We had seen the doctor leaving town as we went after the load. He'd waved at Papa and shouted that, over in Round Valley, Nelly Simmon's baby was causing a great rumpus over getting born. We knew we wouldn't be able to get him for hours.

Mama came running back with Rollo. She had some towels in her arms. For bandages, I guess. July opened her eyes in the water and tried to smile at us and then she fainted again. Papa lifted her out and carried her home. We helped Mama pull off her wet clothes. Her stomach was swollen and already turning blue, but she didn't cry or moan very much. When we'd slipped her nightgown on (Mama had slit it up the back to make it easy), Papa came in with Brother Duke. He and Papa administered to her and in a little while July went to sleep.

"Now don't you worry, Kate, the child will be all right. I know the Lord has heard our prayers." Papa's voice was firm and reassuring. I don't know about the rest of the family, but I stopped worrying and went outside to help unload the hay, not even caring that in the excitement I'd lost Tyler's wide-brimmed straw hat and the sun was doing my neck and face to a turn.

When the doctor came by that night, he gave July some medicine—paregoric, I think—and shook his head over her bruised middle. She didn't eat much and stayed in bed for about a week, but she was up and around after that, none the worse. We thanked the Lord every night and morning for her "narrow escape from death" and pretty soon forgot to thank Him for that. There were other things to thank Him for.

About the middle of December, Mama had a very vivid dream. She told us about it at the breakfast table.

"I dreamed Tyler was working on this ranch, a big one west of here. He saved his money and he had really worked for it. He was planning to come home for Christmas and bring all of us presents and he stopped in a big town on his way home, to buy them. It seems like, it's kinda misty here, that he met some fancy woman and she asked him to go into a pool hall with her."

We gasped at that, because though we knew about pool halls and fancy women, Papa being the marshal and all, it was shameful having your own brother getting familiar with the lower element. Even in a dream.

"He forgot about your song, Papa. You know, 'Keep away from the gals and the . . .' "*

* From the song "Come Over Here, My Son," printed in full at the end of this book.

"Be quiet, Emily Ellen. What did he do then, Mama?"

"Well, then he was gambling. Poor boy." She shook her head. "He thought he was going to double his wages."

Papa was listening to Mama's dream with a frown of concern on his face.

"But he lost it? He lost all his money?"

"Yes, he lost it, and he not only lost his money but he bet the new suit he'd just bought and he lost that, too."

"Then what did he do?"

"He went down to the depot in the dirty old striped pants the man who won his suit had given him, and a terrible yellow and brown and green, I think, checked coat and he climbed in a cattle car and he came home. And I was so glad to see him, that was Christmas present enough."

That was Mama's dream. The next morning there was a knock on the kitchen door as we were eating breakfast.

"Come in."

"I can't," said Tyler's voice through the door. "I've got lice."

Papa jerked open the door and there was Tyler dressed as Mama had described him, in grease-spotted striped pants and the bilious coat, broke and browned from his stay in Nevada.

Papa carried the round tub and water to the granary, where they scoured Tyler, shivering in the cold, with lye soap. He did have lice, or something that looked like them.

Not until Papa had thoroughly decontaminated him was he allowed into the house. Mama hugged him joyously, her head hardly coming to his shoulder.

We excitedly recounted Mama's dream and he, astounded, said all of it except the part about the fancy woman was true. The fancy woman he would not admit to, but I privately thought that he was just being gentlemanly.

All of us were home for Christmas and that was the most important thing about it. Tyler and Rollo brought a tree down from the hills along with a bagful of rabbits they'd shot on the way back. Mama froze them in the snow after they were skinned and cleaned, and with pork chops and chicken they were wonderful for Christmas dinner.

On Christmas Eve we had a sing. Papa sang "Come Over Here, My Son" and "Before the Bright Sun Rises over the Hill" and danced to "The Man on the Flying Trapeze" and each of us contributed to the program. Some of the neighbors came in and Tyler popped dishpans full of corn and poured melted butter over it. We ate fudge and divinity that the twins and I had made and Mama played the Jew's harp. We were treated to a performance of "Cinderella"—starring Emily Ellen (who also directed), with Marybeth and Jeanne as the wicked sisters, Jeremy as the Prince, Davy as the messenger from the King, and Rollo as the wicked stepmother. I have never seen a finer presentation. Marybeth and Jeanne could not have been better cast.

Jeremy felt that his part as the Prince had been played down and he sang "I Am a Mormon Boy" for us, and then Tyler sang "The Holy City" while the skin on my arms goose-bumped in response.

In prayers that night, Papa thanked the Lord for the bounteous crops, the health and strength of the family; he thanked Him for bringing Tyler back to us safely; he thanked Him for the miracle of July's life and for the blessings of family harmony. And he thanked Him especially for the love of a good wife; for the like of her, any man should be willing to crawl on his knees for a thousand miles. It was sort of a roundabout compliment, I thought, but it was well received. Mama glowed.

There was an orange in each of our stockings, some hard candies, and a package. This was our Christmas. But in addition Mama had made us all new dresses or new shirts, and Rollo had helped Papa buy us each a pair of new shoes. Rollo gave me a copy of the Lambs' *Tales from Shakespeare,* and I was wealthy!

On Christmas Day, Aunt Sally and her brood came to pay us a visit. They had been in town for a while, but had been staying with Mama's oldest sister. Now Mama was hard-pressed to find beds for them all. We had to bring in the straw mattresses from the top of the granary and the house swarmed.

I don't think Aunt Sally's prolonged visit had anything much to do with it, but Tyler left home again. He didn't leave a note this time. He told Mama he was going. He packed his few things in one of the old grips Papa had used on his Mission. He said that it still wasn't any different. Everything had to be done Papa's way. Here, he could work for Papa, but nothing was ever his. There were so many of us, taking turns to wash, to eat, to use the toilet. He had told Papa that he ought to build another one and put up "Ladies" and "Gents" signs.

But he didn't go so far away this time—only to Park City. He got a job working in the mines there. But he might as well have gone to Timbuktu for all that we heard from him. Papa and Mama felt bad about his going, but they felt even worse when finally he came back home again, this time to stay.

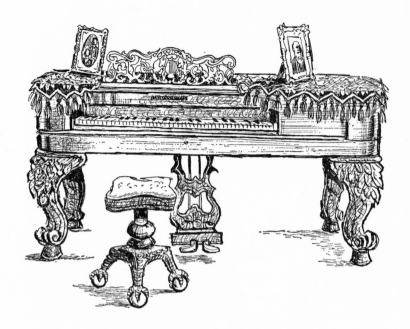

[CHAPTER TWELVE]

I HAD a dream once that Grandfather Campbell came to visit me. He had died many years before the dream. He seemed extraordinarily joyous and I asked him why this was so. He answered rather cryptically, and before I could get him to explain, I woke up. He said: "You have to die before you can know what living is all about. When you are alive you have no perspective." I don't know how much perspective dying gives you, but it is certainly true that while you are living through an event it oftentimes assumes a much greater, or lesser, importance than the years prove it to deserve.

There was one night before time had separated us, before 1918, before marriage and death and the small machinery of daily living had built up fences that we could not seem to find time to climb over.

This was one of the rare evenings when all of us were home. June and July were sitting on the north porch spooning with their beaus. Both Duncan Mitchill and Clay Winston could sing. All four of them were in an operetta once, and as often happens, romantic leads in plays carry over into real life. In this case, the roles took like a vaccination. From that production Duncan and Clay were a part of the Woodrow family.

I was playing the piano quietly for Grandma, and Papa came in and asked me to play "In the Gloaming." When the rest of the family heard him singing they came in, one or two or three at a time, until all of us were there sitting on the floor, the little ones curled up on Grandma's bed, the rest of us gathered around the piano. We sang everything we knew. "Annie Laurie," "Comin' thro' the Rye," "Drink to Me Only." Papa sang all of his special songs that were part of our lives—"Come Over Here, My Son," "The Man on the Flying Trapeze," "Before the Bright Sun Rises over the Hill," "Come Home Early Tonight, My Dear Boy." Grandma, more than a little quavery, sang "White Felither O Lay," and Mama played the Jew's harp. This was a special skill of Mama's that none of us ever acquired. She carried her harp around in her pocket and at the oddest times she would pull it out and twang away. It was a U-shaped piece of metal with a wire string across it, and she played it by somehow changing the shape of her mouth. It played only one note, but it had melody and we could even dance to it. She played "Have You Ever Been into an Irishman's Shanty?" "The Girl I Left Behind Me," and some odd little Irish-jig melodies, the names of which I cannot remember.

We sang "We Thank Thee, O God, for a Prophet" and "My Country, 'Tis of Thee."

But the evening for me was when Rollo sang "With Someone Like You" in his fine clear tenor. Ted Davis had come in with him, and when he finished the first verse and chorus, Ted joined in and Tyler and then the twins and their Duncan and Clay and Emily Ellen, who was developing the deep contralto for which the Woodrow women were known. Papa had stopped singing and he and Mama and Grandma suddenly became the older generation.

They sat and listened and I saw the tears run down Grandma's face and thought she was getting old and sentimental. But now, I know, that maybe Grandma was the only one who had lived long enough to get a perspective on the moment. Perhaps she was the only one who knew that long after she and Mama and Papa were put to rest on the hill, long after the house became empty of Woodrows, echoes of our singing would be lingering in its corners. I do know that each of us preserved that evening in his own way, for we have talked of it since and to all of us it is precious.

There are other times that are always discussed when two or more of us meet. One of them is the night the spirits came to visit.

Papa had gone block teaching. For him this was usually a full evening's visiting, sometimes more than that. Though the Ward was divided so that block teaching was not a burden, no more than eight or ten houses at the most, Papa would get so carried away in bringing the word of the Lord that he usually turned each home that he visited into a cottage meeting. I believe this practice is frowned upon now, for the message is usually a brief one and the visitor is not supposed to stretch it into an evening's sermon. Papa stretched it, and people welcomed him. His sincerity was so clearly evident as he preached, and sincerity is a precious thing—not easily found or kept. I have often felt that people liked me just because I was his daughter and they loved him.

It was about nine o'clock. Mama had put the younger children to bed and had gone, tired, to bed with them. I was reading in my room. June, July, Rollo, and Davy were in the living room. It was the living room now, for a few months before, Grandma had quietly slipped away in her sleep. Mama had divided her belongings with her sisters and sisters-in-law and we had the claw-legged table, the folding bed, and the lovely purple-blue china that Grandma had cherished to remind us of her. Only a few days before she died, she gave Marybeth her little black padded rocker, and to me she gave a crystal sugar bowl which I loved. Grandfather Campbell's high-backed rocker still sat in the living room waiting for Jason to claim it when he found time, but most of Grandma was gone. Papa had replaced the high carved bed with a sofa, which could be made into a bed, of course, and two big leather chairs old Lisha Johnson had built for him in exchange for pasture in the summer for his three cows.

Across the room from the couch was a daybed which had two wings which when lifted up provided sleeping room for two. June and July had pre-empted this bed and this room. After being chaperoned by Grandma through all of their teens, it must have been rather a relief to entertain Duncan and Clay without such close supervision.

The twins, ready for bed, had been sewing on their trousseaus. Rollo had just finished a game of checkers. Davy stacked the checkers in their box and hid the box on the under railing of the couch, safe from Marybeth and Jeanne. Rollo went into the kitchen for a final block of wood so the firelight would dance on the ceiling when the lights were turned out, and while he was gone the twins slipped into bed.

Rollo waited by the door while Davy blew out the lamp, and as he turned the wick down, it happened.

June screamed. In my room, I jumped out of bed. Mama came running. I got to the north door as Rollo fell over the kitchen step trying to get back into the room.

"Light the lamp, light the lamp, we're being killed," July was yelling now. There was a lot of thumping and stamping over in the corner where the daybed was and I kept feeling that if I didn't duck I'd get hit with something.

Rollo lighted the lamp. The noise ceased. June and July, badly rumpled, piled off the cot as if pursued, and words, a jumble of them, poured all over us.

"There's something in this room!"

"I swear it's an elephant. There's an elephant under our bed!"

It was funny and I laughed. They turned on me in fury. "Miss Smarty, Miss Know-it-all. See for yourself. Get on that bed. I dare you!"

Rollo was grinning, too. "Is this another prank of yours?" they stormed at him.

"Now, girls, fun is fun," Mama said, "but it's late and you've waked the babies. All of you get in bed and go to sleep."

"Mama! We can't. There's an elephant under the bed."

Rollo went over and looked under the bed. There was nothing. I was looking under it from its foot and he winked at me. "It's spooks, Prilly. You scared?"

"No," I lied, because suddenly I was.

"Get on it, Prilla, get on it. I dare you!" So I lay down on the cot and nothing happened.

"Turn the lamp down, Davy. I think you have to turn the lamp down."

The lamp went out and the bed began to heave. First the head went up, then the foot. I was clinging to stay on the thing. Something went skimming across my face; I thought it was June's corset. I could hear the checkers shaking in their box and suddenly being thrown, scattering on the floor. A horse, a big one, I thought, was kicking the south wall.

"Let me off! Rollo, let me off!" Rollo had the lamp.

"There really is something. I'd think it was you two, but both of you couldn't heave that bed around with me on it like that. Mama, we've really got a ghost!"

By this time Marybeth and Jeanne were up and both of them were enjoying it. Jeanne sat down on the floor in her white flannel nightgown and held her toes delightedly. Marybeth took over the lamp.

"Rollo, you have a turn."

"Don't turn out the lamp again. It's too hard to light it." Marybeth took the lamp, went into the bedroom, and closed the door.

As soon as Rollo was on the bed and the door was shut, the thumping and the rattling and the shaking started up. Marybeth came back in with the lamp and Mama took her turn. We investigated. Rollo went outside, though obviously the disturbance was in the house. June and July huddled together in one of the chairs. Davy and I looked under the bed again. The checkers were neatly arranged in the box. June's corsets were folded under the rest of her clothes on the piano bench. The thing was baffling, but we were all sure that there was a foreign presence in the house. I do not know whether it is more frightening to be alone when something inexplicable happens, or to be in a company. When one is alone, there is always the logical explanation of hallucinations or imagination, or a nightmare, but when a half dozen people share the incident then it takes upon it frightening proportions.

"I know what is is." Marybeth was pleased with herself. "It's Grandma Campbell, she's come back. She doesn't like it in heaven!"

"Don't be so silly," July snapped. "Grandma Campbell never made that much noise in all her life."

As long as the light was on, everything was calm, but we could feel the imminence of something about to happen, so we left the lamp lit. Marybeth coaxed for us to do it again, and Jeanne wanted to ride on the bed, but Mama would not allow it. Davy sat at the table with disbelief on his face, and I was scared.

"Go get the baby," Mama said to me. "I do not feel it is safe for him to be in there by himself."

So I went into the bedroom and grabbed Jeremy from his bed. Although the lamps were on, shadows loomed large on the ceiling and I was terrified. I hurried back to the living room to wait for Papa, for though the presence seemed to be in that room, so was everyone else.

Papa had two tried and trusted remedies. Tobacco for all sick cattle and prayer for all other ills—physical, mental, or, as in this case, unnatural. "We will have prayers," he said, and we knelt while he asked simply that the spirit or presence which was bringing terror to the hearts of his loved ones be exorcised and sent from this house, never to enter therein again.

When we arose from our knees, Papa, to make sure all temptation was removed, took the checkers from their hiding place and tossed them into the potbellied stove.

The stove roared as if in protest and grew red hot on its sides, but the checkers burned quickly and Papa poked at them to see that they were gone.

"Take the lamp out now." Papa smoothed back the quilts on the cot and laid himself down. Davy took the lamp out and the room was dark, still, and very peaceful.

"That'll do it," Papa announced. "Tell Davy to bring back the light. For tonight, you girls take down the folding bed and I'll sleep here in the cot to make sure of things."

The night passed quietly and our checker-throwing intruder did not return.

Papa was more concerned over the incident than he allowed us to believe, for he went on one of his rare trips to Salt Lake City to see the President. He came back with reassurance.

"The Brethren," he reported "told me that it has been known that on occasion playful spirits enter homes, usually where there are children. They have been said to demonstrate in a noisy manner and often to throw things about. 'Your experience was no doubt one of these playful spirits, but return home and assure your family that a reoccurrence is not at all likely.' "

Reassured, we accepted that night as just one of the not quite usual things that happened to us. Perhaps because we were all familiar with accounts of visits by the eternally wandering Three Nephites, such things were not much more than interesting topics for conversation. (The Three Nephites, sole survivors of an ancient white race that peopled the Americas, were, like John the Beloved, supposed to have been given freedom from death until the Second Coming of the Savior. In the early days of the Church, they went about performing small miracles and bestowing blessings on the deserving.)

It was in my last year of high school that I walked in the Footsteps, and when it happened it did not seem much more than odd, but later years plague me with the mystery, and I have never found a satisfactory explanation.

I had stayed overnight with my friend Josephine, who lived two blocks west and a half block south of us. During the night the first snow of the season fell, and in our little mountain town a snowfall of twelve to eighteen inches was not unusual. This snowfall was within that depth and I had no galoshes. I knew that by the time I waded through it all the way home, my shoes would be ruined. When new shoes came only on Christmas or perhaps the Fourth of July through hard labor, concern for them is great.

It was much too early for the little wooden V-shaped horse-pulled snowplow to have reached our end of town, and the sidewalks were not cleared. The roads awaited, as usual, wagon wheels and horses' hooves to pack them down. There were few automobiles and most of these were prudently blocked up for the winter.

I plunged off the porch into the snow, but at the gate I discovered that a big-footed early riser had walked down the sidewalk going south. The man had worn flat-soled heavy winter galoshes, probably the kind that had triple metal clasps across the front to keep them tightly closed. Papa had a pair that made tracks similar to these, though Papa's were considerably smaller.

I blessed the unknown shoe saver and started north, walking in his southbound steps. I had to stretch my legs to place my feet where his had been and it was awkward sort of jumping and lurching.

When I reached the intersection, the steps came from the east, down the middle of the road. Thankful that they came from the direction I was going, I walked eastward, taking care to see that I landed in the center of each step. At the place where I must turn off the road to the path leading to our gate, the steps stopped!

Unbelieving, I stood in the last set of steps. On all sides lay an unbroken expanse of snow. The wide road stretched out on either side, and now the sun made it glisten with millions of diamonds of light. There were no wagon tracks and Papa had not yet cleared the path from our house to the road.

The steps had begun where I stood, in the middle of the road. The man had just started to walk from that spot! I stood until my feet were numb from cold and wet was seeping into my shoes, then I broke a new trail from the road to our gate.

Papa was at breakfast, but he wiped his mustache and left his cereal and eggs to cool while he came with me. Clearly he could see the big tracks and my footsteps inside them. I thought it was possible for someone to have walked backward and then forward again, but the only double track inside the clear-cut one was my own, both easily defined.

"Mmmm," he said. "Mmmmm. That is a funny one!" But he hadn't finished his chores; he had paths to shovel and his breakfast was waiting. I was near to being late for school and I had an unbroken record for punctuality and attendance nagging at me to hurry.

Papa stroked his chin and twirled his mustache. "There's only one possibility." He didn't say, but I knew what he meant. But why did one of the Three Nephites think saving my shoes was so important?

I hurried through breakfast and getting ready. When we reached the road again, someone had driven a team down the middle of the road. The tracks were still discernible, but no longer mysterious.

Not until sometime later when the importance of perfect attendance had slid into its proper place did I wonder why I had not turned around and followed the footprints to where they were going. Saving my shoes was certainly not the mission of that early walker. But I know, truly, that it was not all hurry and lack of thought . . . I would never have dared to follow, and neither, I think, would Papa.

There were other strangenesses which we accepted easily. Mama's dreams were one of them. It was another dream and Mama's frantic insistence that sent Papa out at night into one of the severe August thunderstorms which bombarded us each summer.

Since lambing time in the spring, Rollo had been working with Uncle John's sheep. He had a mare called Tassel, and Tassel, like too many of Papa's horses, could outrun and outjump most of the horses in the county, but didn't have her full allotment of horse sense. It was a weekend and Rollo had been planning to visit Nelly Dawn Giles over in Round Valley the first time Uncle John rode out to relieve him for a couple of days.

The storm was rolling in, noisy and menacing, when he left camp, but that didn't worry him. He was used to storms. There had hardly been a summer when lightning, disproving the old adage, hadn't struck either our block or the Montgomerys' across the street. They'd lost horses and cows; we'd lost two giant cottonwoods and a haystack. The lightning had carried out Uncle John's dire threat of a horrible death for Blackie. Her disposition hadn't sweetened when Papa came home from his Mission and she was still too mean to sell and gave too much milk to kill, even if most times after she'd given a nice foamy, creamy pail, she'd haul off and kick it over. I knew where Mama's "Don't kick over your bucket of milk" came from when she chided us for making too much of something admirable we had done.

The storms lent meaning to Papa's furious "thunder and lightning" when he swore. They rumbled and shrieked through our trees and around our house with such intensity that they left their mark on all of us. Either you were scared to death when the storm began and huddled in the living room as Mama and the twins did, not daring to go into the next room. ("If your next breath is going to be your last, you don't want to draw it alone.") Or you enjoyed the violence and fury of weather, maddened and enraged by boredom, no doubt, and shrugged it off as an elemental temper tantrum. Rollo felt that way, Papa did, and I did. I think the rest of the family would gratefully have forgone the storms and suffered a little drought.

"It's going to be a humdinger, boy. You'd better wait it out," warned Uncle John. But Rollo pulled on his slicker, turned up his hat brim, and rode off into the rain.

Currant Creek was roiling when he tried to cross. The

light footbridge had been swept away, but the stream was narrow and Tassel was a born steeplechaser, or at least she and Rollo thought so. They were both wrong.

He rode away from the stream and then, turning, dashed downhill toward it, daring the mare. It was Nelly Dawn or the sheep camp, and clearly there was no real choice. The mare cleared the water but slipped on the bank and fell. Rollo jumped, but his foot caught in the stirrup and the mare rolled on him, breaking his leg below the knee, the same leg he'd broken in the "airplane crash."

Tassel scrambled up the bank and stood waiting for him. He had fallen in a clump of willows, which held him firmly, just out of reach of the rushing water. There he stayed, afraid to drag himself farther up the bank, for at any time the clutch of the willows might slacken and allow him to slip into the stream where he would be helpless.

Here Papa found him as Mama had seen him in her dream, groaning in pain and covered with mud, in the first clump of willows north of where the footbridge should be. Tassel nickered as Big Red scrabbled over the other side of the bank and Papa had no trouble at all finding him. He had a bit of trouble getting him onto the horse, broken leg and all. He'd cut his leg, not too bad, above his knee, and though it had bled a lot, he got blood poisoning in it, so he limped around the house for another summer. I can't remember any time that Rollo was hurt that it wasn't his legs. Always, his strong, sturdy, muscular legs.

Mama dreamed about unimportant things, too, but these special dreams had a clarity, she said, that was not like a dream. She knew that they were real. When she dreamed, as she did later, about Rollo's child and his concern for her, that was the last time, for she wept and said she did not want to know these things. In prayer on that morning in the "special manner" part, Papa asked that his good wife Catherine be not afflicted with knowing, and she had no more such dreams.

The mysteries in our house would have driven anyone who believed in the logic of cause and effect rapidly insane.

I wondered about the dreams and asked Papa why Mama had them. He shrugged his shoulders and pulled his mustache and answered me with his eyes. If there was anything that couldn't be explained by the Scriptures, Papa, or Atty Wootten, the Central School principal, you chalked up one for the Three Nephites. If they obviously couldn't be involved, you resorted to the all-prevalent theory of "sometime we'll understand." This reduced everything to "living equals dying" and the simple acceptance of it that is inevitable.

[CHAPTER THIRTEEN]

DEATH HELD no fear for us: only the circumstances which brought it about were sometimes shocking and good-byes were often almost unbearable. "Good-bye is a little death, death is a big good-bye," Mama said. We said good-bye a lot.

Papa liked a fast trotting horse and he'd bought a brood mare from somewhere that mothered some nice colts. The first colt, a happy, prancing little fellow, he had given to Tyler for his twelfth birthday. I've never seen Tyler as pleased over anything except Margaret, but she came a lot later. Tyler always hurried through his chores so he could brush the colt and turn it out in the lot and watch it play.

"A horse," he told me with certainty, "is the most beautiful living thing." He got a pad and sketched his colt. His drawings were very good, I thought.

"Prettier than a baby? Prettier than Mary Ellen?"

Tyler considered and said thoughtfully: "I think maybe so. See how his lines just flow, and you wouldn't think they could be so beautiful, up on their stilty legs like they are."

I agreed that Tyler's horse was beautiful, but I thought that it was one of those dumb things about boys and men, they sure had difficulty knowing what was what.

I told Papa about Tyler's drawings and Papa asked to see them. He thought they were good, too, and he made a frame for the biggest one and hung it in the living room. He showed it to people when they came in and Tyler was pleased and brought his pictures to Papa at night. The growing resentment over having to do what Papa said when he said it, seemed to be wearing away. Then one afternoon Papa had to make a hurried trip to Wallsburg, and to keep the colt from following the mare, he tied it to the wagon wheel, but the colt bucked and struggled and somehow got its head caught in the spokes of the wheel.

When we came home from school the colt was dead, and Tyler had an awful time with that good-bye.

Papa would have given Tyler the next colt, but he had promised it to Rollo, and he couldn't very well break his word. The second one was very like the first; it had the same sire. Its front legs were white and we didn't have to think much about what to name it. Nothing was going to happen to this little beauty, and we spoiled Lady Stockings almost as much as we did Emily Ellen. She was gentle and sweet, not nearly as prancy as her brother had been. She followed us around and I heard Mama telling Papa that the horse didn't know she was a horse. I don't think she did, either. Papa rode the mare downtown to get his hair cut one day. The barber owned the saloon and had set up his shop in the back of it. When the saloon wasn't busy the barbershop was. I really think the man showed a lot of enterprise. There were many men in our town, I heard Papa tell Mama, who wouldn't have liked to have the Bishop see them going into the saloon, but who could lift his eyebrows if you were going in to get a haircut?

Somebody else going in, naturally to get a haircut, left the door open and Stockings went in after him to find Papa. Papa thought it was funny, as he would, but the barber didn't, and he waved things at Stockings that made her nervous, and she had an accident on the saloon floor. Papa said that was a fitting place, as the saloon ought to be closed up anyway, and Papa lost another vote. Mama had to buy some barber scissors and cut his hair because that was the only barbershop in town at the time.

Papa said Mama should go into the business, it was the best haircut he'd had in years. But I thought it went up a little too high in places, and Tyler rode his horse all the way to Midway to get his hair cut. That wasn't anything unusual for him. Papa wouldn't let him walk through the saloon anyway, but Tyler evidently didn't think that Mama was as good a barber as Papa did.

After that, Papa called the colt Barber, and she answered to that as well as Lady or Stockings. My, she was sweet.

We had to say good-bye to her, too, before we'd ever had a chance to ride her. It was a hot day and the milkman had left half a can of whey when he brought the milk cans back. We thought that'd be a refreshing change from water on such a hot day; horse lemonade, we said it was. Stockings liked it. She drank a lot of it. But then she got colic, and though Rollo and Tyler went looking for Papa, they didn't find him soon enough. All the tobacco mixture that Papa poured down her (if tobacco was good for all sick cattle, as the Doctrine and Covenants said, it'd be good for horses, too) couldn't save her. That good-bye wasn't easy, either.

For the colts, we had funerals, as we did for all the other pets which we loved and lost. The corner of the pasture lot was a beloved plot of ground. On Decoration Day we gathered bouquets and put them on the graves. We felt a closeness and prayed that, when we got to Heaven, Tyler's Prince and Rollo's Lady, along with Tatters and Kittybelle and Muffin, would be there, too.

Jeremy buried his magpie there, and even after I had married and "put away childish things," it warmed me sweetly to see Rollo's child busily working in the Pet Yard, straightening the wooden markers and putting flowers on the little graves.

Only the family came to these funerals and the grief of the bereaved was shared by all of us. They were brief and dignified good-byes that we knew would be only temporary, for "are not five sparrows sold for two farthings, and not one of them is forgotten before God?"

It was when Boot and Frances left that I really knew what Mama meant when she said "Good-bye is a little death."

A few days after Uncle Lew had brought them, when the "move over a little, you're crowding" feeling wore off, when Mama had found a corner for their homemade table and chairs and doll cupboard, when she had made a space in Rollo's drawer for Boot's things and a space in Emily Ellen's for Frances's, and when Papa had thanked the Lord "for the privilege bestowed upon us in His wisdom, to care for these motherless little ones," they were welded into the family.

Both of Aunt Mag's children were a little quieter than we were. They didn't seem to get into as much trouble, or at least didn't seem to begin it. Frances was fond of Grandma and she waited on her, running her errands, fixing her cups of tea. A firm defender of the Word of Wisdom, Papa seemed to realize that Grandma's comforts were few and trials were many, and when Grandma sipped, Papa never seemed to know that it was tea that she was drinking. If he had, he would have been forced to remind her that she would be forfeiting a blessing. When I asked Mama about it, she looked at me over the tops of her eyeglasses while she was stitching away and said: "Prilla, your Grandma's stored up so many blessings she can afford to forfeit a few." So Grandma drank her tea which Frances made for her so carefully. And the only time it was ever brought to mind was when Marybeth generously offered to make it in Frances's absence.

"You like your tea, Grandma?" she asked.

"It's fine, honey."

"Doesn't it taste a little different?" Grandma sipped and smacked, testing it.

"Nooo, I don't think it does."

"Well it should." Marybeth was disappointed. "I spit in it."

One day Uncle Lew drove up unannounced and introduced his new wife. He thanked Mama and Papa for taking care of his children (for twelve years) and said that now they were old enough for him to manage them. He had a place and he'd come to take them home.

Mama was shocked.

"Lew," she remonstrated, "they're ours. We've nursed 'em, fed 'em, clothed 'em. We've been their mother and father. You can't take them. I'm not going to allow it."

"I appreciate what you did, Kate, and though I haven't written much, I really do thank you for it all, but now I've got a farm and a place for them. I'm married and Elly can see to them. They'll be well taken care of."

"Now that they're big enough to be some help, you mean." Mama was bitter, and Papa stepped in. "Now, Kate."

"They've been here since they were babies!" She wouldn't be stopped. "You can't just uproot children and take them away from their family!"

"We're their family. Elly and I. They're mine, Kate. I'm sorry, but there's nothing you can do about it."

Uncle Lew came striding out of the kitchen and told Boot and Frances to pack their things. They cried and we cried and Grandma drew Uncle Lew into her room. What she said had no more effect on him than what Mama had said, for evidently he did not "honor the aged," as Papa did. When Grandma came out she was crying, and Frances had to be dragged down the path and out the gate, pleading for Mama to come and get her. Mama would have, too, except Papa firmly held her back and kept saying: "There is absolutely nothing we can do. He's within his rights. You knew it when you took them. Hush, Kate, now hush."

Grandma worried and fussed and grieved for Frances and not one of us had quite Frances's touch with a pillow at the small of her back or the timing with a hot little pot of tea.

Grandma wasn't the only one who missed them. Boot was another shoulder to help the boys push the girls' tightly held door open, he was a hand in the field, he could pick up more potatoes than any of us, and he was tireless at filling the woodbox. He didn't mind picking the raspberries and the gooseberries. He had his place in the family, he filled in a bare spot. When the older boys were late, Boot could, and did, milk the cows with a smile and never accepted the offer of a nickel from an older brother who knew that he would get a Scotch Blessing if Papa found him shirking.

When Boot and Frances had gone, the beds felt empty, and the house felt hollow. They were our brother and our sister and we missed them and prayed for them at night and in the morning. But their homesick little notes did not reach us often, for they did not have the pennies to buy stamps. There was never a letter that came that Mama and Grandma did not weep for the poor little things away from home, and Mama would rage. It was terrible for a while, but school started and we sort of spread out like one tooth will when another has been pulled and it was not so painful after a while.

Uncle Lew did not bring them back to us, as we prayed for him to do, and it was only when they were grown that we found that Grandma and Mama's "specials"—packages of cookies and candy, fruitcake, hair ribbons, any little thing that Mama could manage out of her egg money—were the bright spots in their lives and enabled them to adjust more cheerfully to this new and harder world, knowing that they were a loved and wanted part of our family.

For a long time, Papa would call out "Boo-oot!" when he could see the woodbox was empty, and the first time he checked us out for Sunday school after they had gone, he said: "This is an awful short lineup this morning. Who's still in bed?" Then he jammed on his hat and led the procession down the walk. "C'mon," he said. "We haven't got all day."

Mama never did forgive Uncle Lew. She had always told us that hating anyone was a waste of time. "You've only got so much energy," she said. "Hate uses a lot of it up. Use your energy to build up, not tear down."

"You don't always practice what you preach, do you, Mama?" I asked her when she was discussing Uncle Lew with venom one afternoon. Papa had been telling her that they were Lew's kids and Lew was enough of a father to take good care of them.

"What do you mean, miss?" she asked me sharply.

"You know, about how you're not supposed to hate anyone. It's such a waste of energy. You're sure wasting a lot on Uncle Lew."

"It doesn't take very much energy to hate him," she snapped. And I guess it didn't; she seemed to get a lot of other things done.

Grandma Campbell had been ailing for months before she died and we'd had the Elders to administer to her and been quiet but it didn't seem to help. Mama and Papa took turns sleeping on a cot in the living room, where she had lived all this time. She hadn't sung much for a year or two, so it was no surprise when Mama woke the twins to tell them to run down and tell Uncle Jim that Grandma was dead. On the way down there, in the middle of the night, a horse wandering around loose in the schoolyard chased them and they were too scared to come back home alone. Uncle Jim and Aunt Sarah came back with them, but Johnny Winterrose had already come and taken Grandma down to the funeral parlor.

Everybody went to the funeral except me and the Trio. Mama said I was big enough to stay at home and keep the fires burning and tell the Relief Society Sisters where the dishes were kept. The Trio were sent over to Mrs. Bond's to be kept clean until the folks came back. Then they could be sent home presentable, to be seen and not heard.

Grandma's good-bye, though I loved her more than the colts, was easier than theirs and lacked the heartbreak of Boot's and Frances's going. She was there one night when I went to bed and, by the time all the company left, most of her things had been taken away and Grandma was happily united with Grandfather Campbell and Grandma Muz. Everybody said so.

[CHAPTER FOURTEEN]

NINETEEN FOURTEEN was the year of big events. Tyler got married. We were hardly aware that he was serious about a girl, or even knew one that well. We didn't see him often and when we did he was quiet about the girl, as he was about everything else. But he loved Margaret. You could tell the way his eyes followed her every movement and how he watched the door when she was outside with the twins. She was a beautiful little thing. Big brown eyes that snapped and black hair that curled, like Marybeth's, down to her shoulders. She was quick and bright and I thought, old Tyler is going to have to speed up his pace now.

Mama was crushed that Tyler hadn't written us about the wedding.

"Now, Mama," he drawled, a week after, when they had stopped by on their way to Park City after their brief honeymoon. "Now, Mama, I didn't want any fuss, and if you had known there was a wedding in the offing, I'd been dragged into a lot of folderol that would have downright turned my stomach."

"Every girl should have a wedding. It wasn't fair to Margaret. Dragging her up before the justice of the peace, or whatever you did. Why it isn't even legal!"

Margaret intervened. "We went to Salt Lake," she said softly. "We were married in the Temple. That's the way Tyler wanted it, and as long as I got Tyler, I didn't care if there was no one else there."

Mama was mollified. The marriage was legal, anyway.

Mama piled their wagon with wedding gifts. Pieced quilts and chicken-feather pillows, cured ham, jellies, bottled fruits and vegetables, dried beans, fresh vegetables from the garden, six white Leghorn hens, eggs, butter, a braided rug, and two pairs of Grandmother Campbell's beautiful crocheted-on pillowcases. The pillowcases were Mama's treasures and she packed them away in tissue to save a pair for each of us when we married.

Archduke Francis Ferdinand and his wife Sophie were assassinated in Bosnia, and everybody said this started the war that Papa had been reading us rumors about from the Bible, and people talked about whether the President would be able to keep us out of it. At that time the war seemed far away, a million miles or more, but it kept getting closer.

June and July announced their engagements. They weren't planning to be married for a year or so because they had to get their trousseaus ready and that took time. Papa was well pleased with their choices. He said he felt that he'd practically reared those boys; anyway they'd been mooning on our doorsteps for so long it was a relief for them to finally declare their honorable intentions. He insisted that he be asked formally for his daughters' hands in marriage.

I don't know what went on in those interviews, and I was curious about them for years. I do know that the boys were awfully tight-lipped about them. I think Papa gave them a bad time, though, for when Antony Anderson drove up from Salt Lake a few years later to ask Papa if he could marry Emily Ellen, he questioned Duncan and Clay, and then spent the day chopping wood and piling it up against the corral fence. Emily went about her work, occasionally taking him a glass of homemade root beer or a cookie to keep up his strength. She sat for a while on the woodpile and watched him chop, and I watched them through the pantry window. She wore her hair piled up on her head with a few ringlets down the side of her neck. Shapely and slender in her cotton dress, purple blue to match her and Papa's eyes, she was irresistible.

Papa looked out the window and chuckled.

"It's true," he said, "a man will crawl on his knees a thousand miles for the woman he really loves, and I'll be thunder-and-lightninged if I'm going to hand my daughters over to these young fellers unless I know they're going to be taken care of in the manner to which they are accustomed."

"In the manner . . ." I teased him. "You mean, Papa, that they've got to go on taking baths in the round tub in the middle of the kitchen floor and going outside in six feet of snow and twenty degrees below zero to, well, when you have to go? You mean she's got to shine brass buckets every day for the rest of her life, and wash milk cans and pans every morning and night? Emily Ellen told me that Antony's folks are well off. His sisters dress like fashion plates, and they have a bathroom right in their house that has a stretch-out tub and hot and cold running water, and they have a room each.

"Must Emily sleep in the middle of two girls until she gets enough seniority to snag the outside of the bed for herself! Really now, Papa."

He looked a little abashed, and then he said seriously: "Emily is a child of my heart, as are all of you. I want her to find a man that will be good to her, treat her with respect, care for her in sickness and in health for time and all eternity. I want to be sure these fellers know that marriage isn't a game, and that there's some things about it not so pleasant as others."

"Tony's a good boy."

"He's a fine boy, I think. I aim to know more about him and his family. A stretch-out bathtub don't mean much to a woman if she hasn't got a strong shoulder to lean on, and Emily Ellen isn't as sturdy as some of the rest of you. She's cut real fine."

Antony passed inspection and evidently lived up to all his premarital promises. Papa was always pleased with him. That he gave Emily not only a stretch-out bathtub but a swimming pool as well was the least of his accomplishments. He had a strong shoulder.

That summer Rollo bought a Reo. It cost seventeen hundred dollars, and when you went downhill, it would get up to a speed of almost thirty miles an hour. If you happened to be going uphill, which was often, it might go, too, if everybody got out and pushed. The Reo and Tyler's wedding coincided, just about. Although the chivaree was a week or so late, Rollo loaded twenty-two of his cohorts in and on that Reo and, armed with cans, dishpans, and tick-tack-toes, as well as a little likker, they drove over to Park City and chivareed Margaret and Tyler. I guess the party got a little rough, because he came back with only seventeen of the fellows. The rest spent an all-expenses-paid weekend with the marshal over there.

When Rollo wobbled in, minus one carbide headlight and holding up Ted Davis, who was afraid to go home "in this condition," Mama was remarkable.

"Prilla," she warned me severely, "you will not say one thing about this to your father." She efficiently put both boys to bed, sent word to Aunt Molly that the boys were spending the day together and not to worry, and alternately carried basins and cold clothes into and out of the bedroom.

"It's disgraceful," snorted June. "Carrying on like that. What will Papa say? And him the city marshal. Why, he'll die of shame!"

"By the time he finds out about it," said Mama, "there won't be much use for that. He'll have to keep right on living!" Marybeth and Jeanne, luckily, were spending the weekend with Aunt Sally and her brood, and, incredibly, they were said to be well behaved. Jeremy didn't seem to know what was going on; free of the girls for a day or two, he sailed blocks of wood in the ditch for hours at a time.

That afternoon, the broken headlight and the mysterious dent in the fender almost gave Rollo a relapse when he viewed the damage, but he drove down to the blacksmith shop and when he brought the car home, after working on it the rest of the day, you couldn't tell, except on close inspection, that it had been out all night.

Papa didn't think much of the Reo, though **Rollo** was generous about letting others use it and would have taught any of us to drive it if we had wished to learn.

"Give me a nice trotting horse any day," Papa said. "I wouldn't trade Diamond out there for all the fancy automobiles in the country. It's downright undignified, to go honking like a goose everytime you make a turn, so you won't smash into another of your wild generation. Pretty soon the roads won't be safe to drive on, the way this auto traffic is getting to be."

He wasn't so much in favor of the fine trotting horse a little while later. Diamond disgraced the whole family and certainly didn't do much for Papa in the next election. That fall Papa was running for re-election. Because there was a lot of worry about the European situation and whether or not the President was going to let these fellows settle their own quarrels and keep us out of war, interest in the elections was much greater than I had ever remembered. The Democrats had a picnic out at the new power plant and it was a nice little jaunt in a buggy to get there.

The Governor came up from Salt Lake to speak at the rally, and a parade was formed, with him at the head. The roads were dry, and the further you were back in line, the more dust you ate.

Mama had loaded as many of us as she could in our two-seated buggy and hitched up Diamond. Papa was riding ahead on a saddle horse to lead the way. Mama had never had a very strong hand with horses; our old bay mare was about her speed. Diamond, tired of plodding along in this hot and dull procession, took matters into her own spirited hooves and broke ranks.

Mama was helpless, and Diamond, getting her head,

dashed out. She could never be content with anything in front of her anyway, and in no time at all she had legged it past the Mayor, the City Council, the martial band, her heels spewing dust into their faces and onto their wives' fancy dresses, many of which Mama had made.

"Hang on, girls, for heaven's sake, hang on! I can't hold this horse." We hung on, and Diamond raced passed the Governor's buggy, past Papa, who thundered and light-ninged and whoa-ed her. But she ignored him. Not until she had passed the whole procession and had a two-mile lead did she slow down to a walk and allow Mama to cluck her onward to the power plant.

Papa, bless him, was hard put to keep from laughing when he came to see if we were all right, and the twinkle stayed in his eyes all day, even while the Mayor was telling him severely: "Dave, that's not a fit horse for a man to keep around his place!"

I don't think Papa apologized to the Governor. He was afraid to. Afraid he'd laugh. That night when we were home, he roared. "I have never seen anything so funny in my life! Ain't that mare a dandy fast goer? Now tell me, ain't she a dandy one!"

Mama was embarrassed and subsequently lost a couple of customers, but Papa thought it was hilarious.

"You girls were flouncing around and squealing, and I've never seen Kate in public before with her hair awry. My, that was funny!"

Two days later he didn't think it was so funny. He lost the election and he blamed the horse. He was going out to shoot that thunder-and-lightning horse and sell her for fish food. But the new marshal got banged up in a fight with two drunken pool-hall boys and a couple of transients three days after he took office. Papa was pressed back into service. The marshal resigned, Papa served out his term, and was re-elected faithfully until he "didn't choose to run."

Papa's sense of humor frequently got him into trouble. Especially with Mama. She was a little thing, wore a size-four shoe. She never weighed more than a hundred pounds in her life, even when she was pregnant, and she came almost even with Papa's stickpin. But she carried a wallop. One afternoon, not long after the horse incident, she was gathering the eggs. This task was usually assigned to Marybeth or Jeanne, but Papa had bought a big, leggy red rooster who was aptly named Hannibal. Hannibal aimed to be master of the henyard and he challenged anyone who went into it. He'd chased the little girls out of the coop. I'd hated chickens ever since, and before, the murders in the hay and wouldn't offer. Mama pooh-poohed the chicken's fierceness and marched in to claim her hen-coop rent. The rooster, who was perching atop the henhouse, flew down at her, scratching her face, snagging her collar, and raising a lot of fuss and feathers.

"Dave!" she screamed. "I'm blinded! Help! I'm blinded!" Papa, hearing her screams, ran from the barnyard, and the rest of us ran outside to see why she was screaming. Mama was down on her hands and knees in the dust of the chicken yard. Her face was bleeding and she was crawling in what she thought was the general direction of the gate. I don't know why she was crawling, the rooster hadn't hurt her legs, but she was.

Papa ran to her and picked her up. He carried her solicitously over to the hydrant and washed her face off with his handkerchief.

"Open your eyes, Kate. Open your eyes. Let me see

what's the matter." She was keeping both of them tightly closed, but there weren't any eyeballs hanging out and Papa had stanched the bleeding on her cheek."

"I can't," she sobbed. "That beast has blinded me!"

"Open 'em for me. Let me see," coaxed Papa.

She slowly opened them wider and wider. There was nothing wrong. The rooster had flurried some dust in her eyes, washed out now by her tears.

Papa very slowly set her on her feet and bent over to rinse out his handkerchief. His shoulders were shaking. Lined up along the picket fence, we started to giggle.

"Dave!" Mama peered at him. "Dave Woodrow, are you laughing at me?"

Papa burst out, clutching his stomach. "Ah, hah, hah, hah," he boomed. "Funniest dang thing I ever saw in my life. Ah, hah, hah, hah, hah." But the laughing stopped abruptly.

Mama had picked up a good-sized rock, walked over to where he was sitting on the edge of the trough, and clonked him with it.

"Oh-wee, Kate!" But he saw her flouncing through the gate, banging it with ferocity behind her, and once again he was dissolved in mirth. We laughed, too, until we couldn't stand up.

"Bunch of idiots!" Mama muttered when we finally went in the house. "I've been party to bringing a bunch of idiots to this earth, may the Lord forgive me! And the whole blethering lot of you will get nothing more for dinner than bread and milk, provided you fix it yourselves."

We ate our bread and milk as soberly as we could with Mama sitting there in her rocking chair, not deigning to grace the table. Papa kept his eyes on his bowl. If he'd raised them, we'd have laughed again, and we had been brought up with strict taboos against divorce.

Mama always declared that she was patient and long-suffering, and Papa seriously agreed, but there were times when her Campbell temper flared. What could have turned into a family tempest nearly always ended in laughter. I don't know of anything of which Papa was more proud than "Kate's spunk."

He had bought himself a new coat. Papa's way of getting into a coat was a little different from other men's. He put his arms in somehow, and flipped it with a shrug of his shoulders into place, then he would thrust out his arms sideways as if to loosen it to give his big shoulders play. We were standing in an admiring circle as Papa put on his new coat. Mama went to pat down the lapel just as Papa flung out his arms. His doubled fist hit her on the nose and the blood spurted.

She was trying to stop the blood and stop the tears, and Papa was immediately contrite.

"Hit me," he begged. "Hit me back. I didn't mean to do it, Kate. I'll feel better if you hit me." So she did. She doubled up her fist, and with the biggest swing she could reach for, she bopped him right on the end of his nose. So we ran for another towel and came back to find them both sitting on the floor, laughing and mopping. Papa had more to show than Mama did. Her nose stopped bleeding, but she had ruptured a vein on the end of his and it was to be easily seen the rest of his life. He wore it as a badge of her prowess, much to her embarrassment. He had to get his new coat cleaned, too, before he could wear it.

You'd think that with making a living for our running-over family and the marshal's duties, Papa would have had little time for us, but he always had time, it seemed, to sing to us, to dance, and to play games. When I had done up my hair and wore high heels, I was still racing Papa round the block and getting involved with the rest of the family in his impromptu contests.

Always there was some sort of test of skill and Papa usually beat us, crowing in delight at the fact that we young sprouts couldn't hold a candle to him, an old, middle-aged man. I remember one of these games, a sort of idiot's blind man's buff. You put a can on top of the clothesline post, then put on a blindfold, crossed your arms, took hold of your right ear with your left hand, and with your right hand wildly swung a baseball bat, in an attempt to knock the can off the post. Papa was so certain of this one—I think he'd practiced it—that he offered each of us fifty cents if we could do it. I couldn't. June, July, and Emily Ellen failed, too, along with Davy and Jeremy. Rollo knocked it off easily. "Now you do it, Papa. You challenged us," said Rollo. "You do it."

Papa put on a blindfold, took a powerful swing, and somehow, it happened so fast, hit himself on the head and fell stretched out under the clothesline. He'd knocked himself out!

Mama came rushing out, scolding us for getting Papa mixed up in our fool games, and sat down to put his head in her lap. He must have come to almost immediately, because while Mama was moaning over him: "Are you all right, Dave?" he turned his head slightly and, opening one eye, winked at me. It took her quite a while to get him to regain full consciousness, though, and it wasn't until she ordered Davy to run for Dr. Alexander that he staggered fraudulently to his feet.

I guess the most important thing that happened that year

was that I fell in love. I knew that Colton Hanks was for me the first time I saw him. I'd not been too interested in fellows before. There was school and church and family and also the fear that no matter how broadminded he was you took your chances when you brought a boy home. It required a lot of fortitude to face down Marybeth and Jeanne and Jeremy. I never managed to say hello and good-bye fast enough to escape their questions. "Are you going to marry Prilla? Did you know she has a wart on her big toe? Did you know she writes things down all the time?" And Marybeth's shocking "And she isn't much fun to sleep with. She won't tell more than one story, and she eats crackers in bed."

This kind of thing has a depressing effect on romance, and though June and July laughed and overlooked it, I trembled at the thought of leading some unsuspecting Daniel into this den of man eaters.

Colton was within a year of graduation at the University of Utah. It hadn't been easy for him. He'd had to work his way through. Tall and brown-haired and level-eyed, he had a deep voice and a subtle sense of humor that kept me chuckling long after he'd gone back to Salt Lake. He couldn't manage many trips up, though he rode up a few times on top of the cans of milk on the milk truck to save money. Of this Papa approved. It was adding fact to his "crawl a thousand miles" theory. He believed that true love shouldn't run smoothly, and around our house it never did.

It was 1916 before we felt that we could see our way clear to getting married in another year, and by the time that year dragged its way through all the wanting days and nights, it looked like the President wasn't going to keep us out of war.

The war emptied our house like a pulled plug sends

water swirling down a drain. The first to go were Duncan and Clay, and with them the twins' weddings. They'd kept putting them off for one reason or another, lack of money and the imminence of war mostly. Now they decided to wait. It was much easier being a sweetheart than a wife, they were told so often.

Rollo and Ted Davis drove to Provo to enlist. They had invited their current girl friends to make the drive with them. Mama was shocked when she heard that they were going down unchaperoned and she looked at me. "No," she said, "you'd probably allow anything to go on while you had your nose buried in a book." She sent Emily Ellen.

"My goodness," Emily Ellen told me. "I was embarrassed. The way they kissed those girls. And my own brother! And in front of me! Most of the time I didn't even dare turn around. I got a stiff neck from looking to one side all day." At any rate, Emily Ellen must have served Mama's purpose. They came back that night, not too late. Before Rollo left, he got himself engaged to a beautiful little girl from Provo, not the one he'd invited to drive down with him, either. I think he met Alice, somehow, during the process of enlisting. I'm not quite sure. But Rollo was always fast, like Papa. He moved so swiftly that what he was doing was done before you knew he'd started it. I sort of pitied that poor girl. I thought maybe she'd reaped a whirlwind.

The twins went to Salt Lake to work and to be near their sweethearts until the boys left Fort Douglas. They were stationed there quite a while before they went to Camp Kearney. Boot joined the Navy and came home for a week before shipping out, and Colton Hanks got a commission. He and Boot left the same day and later served on the same ship for a while.

Now at home there was, for the first time, enough room, and I would have traded my roomy bed anytime for a crowded one with laughing girls and whispered secrets.

I lay there at nights and missed Colton and was afraid for him. I walked all the way, every day, down through the school lot, past the blacksmith shop and the Exchange, to peer hopefully into Box 334. For sometimes there would be letters from Colton, two or three, interesting as only he has ever written. He wrote about the weather. "Never have I seen the weather change like this. Yesterday it was summer. Today it is fall. Flip-flop!" When I told him that I pretended to sleep on his shoulder and arranged my pillow so, he wrote back quizzically: "I am not sure that I like being substituted for a pillow."

I missed the noise and July's husky voice cussing some fellow or other. Like when she came down with tick fever and blamed it on a boy from Kamas who kissed her good night more fervently than she liked. She'd never gone with him again, and, crushed, he wrote her lovesick notes. One of July's friends wrote to the boy in July's name and said that she'd go with him to a dance at Kill Care if he'd call for her the next Saturday night. The boy rode down all the way from Kamas and arrived as July was getting into her wrap to go out with Duncan. He was irate and stomped off down the walk muttering inanely.

"Any damn-fool fish can go downstream, but you'll not find many that you can coax to swim up!" That, and the Three Nephites, and the Steps have given me many hours' food for thought.

Our house now seemed very big. Only the Trio, Davy, Emily Ellen, and I were left. Davy wandered about, lost without Rollo, whom he had followed everywhere. He ignored Jeremy, who couldn't do anything right, not even bring in a block of wood without dropping it, and he didn't seem to want to go with Papa, although Papa asked him all the time and was even more lost than Davy was.

Rollo got one furlough home. He'd charmed whoever you have to charm in the Army out of enough time to get married. He said he'd rather leave a lonely wife than a lonely sweetheart. The wedding was sweet and brief and uncrowded. They had two days. I cried all the time and some of my tears were for them.

Alice spent her weekends with us and, after I knew her better, I knew that Rollo had been wise to claim her, for Alice turned men's heads. Whenever I was with her, I could see them stare after her, though, to be sure, she kept her eyes demurely ahead.

The house wasn't empty long. It filled up again to bursting. Aunt Sally came to visit and stayed her usual four months. The songs they sang during that time still make my heart ache. The titles told a common war story. "Over There," "With Someone Like You," "My Buddy," and "Keep the Home Fires Burning." A horrible ballad which I dreaded to hear was gruesomely popular, "The Letter Edged in Black."

[CHAPTER FIFTEEN]

TYLER DIDN'T HAVE to go to war. He had two children, and Papa and Mama found a lot of joy in visiting them in Park City whenever it was possible and in bringing them back for a day or two. Mama said a house just wasn't a house unless there was a baby in it. Margaret was expecting her third child and she wasn't well. Neither was Tyler. The work in the mines was not for a boy reared in fresh air and sunshine. Tyler's pallor and stooped shoulders worried me. They worried Papa, too, and Mama, and whenever Tyler came to visit for an afternoon or anyone was going to Park

City, Mama sent fresh butter and cream and eggs and beef roasts.

"I know they have enough to eat," she fretted, when I helped her pack the boxes. "But he looks bad. It's little enough I can do for him." She wiped her eyes with the corner of her apron.

"Oh, Prilla, it's so easy when they're little and you can cuddle them up to you and love them. A cookie is a wonderful cure for a cut knee. Just about any problem can be solved with a picnic lunch or a batch of fudge. It's when they're older that none of it"—she pointed to the basket—"does any good."

Just before Aunt Sally packed up to leave with her brood and all the things she could "borrow" unnoticed, we put our first Gold Star in the window.

Mama was sick with grief when we got the telegram about Boot. "A gun had exploded during gunnery practice," Colton wrote me, "and Boot was killed." Papa was quieter, and for the first time I noticed that his purple eyes were deep-set and hooded. He looked directly at you with an effort and he didn't find so many things to laugh at.

I didn't care how much of our stuff Aunt Sally took with her. It had always been my task when she visited to see that her loot was kept to a minimum. That Aunt Sally just couldn't help taking things was an accepted fact. I don't think she was ever reproached for it, and certainly she was nonetheless welcome in our house, though it puzzled all of us how she could get away with so much when we watched her so carefully. When we went to visit her, she often displayed what she had taken.

"Kate," she'd say, "have you seen this doily that Mother made for me? I think it's one of the prettiest ones she ever made. It was a twin of one she made for you, I think." And for the first time Mama would find that her "twin" had disappeared. Aunt Sally was cheerful and very witty, though, and during this sad time there wasn't too much to laugh at. We were grateful to her.

My "letter edged in black" came on a Saturday night. Since I was a little girl, Saturday night had been my favorite. The paper boy, when it wasn't June, would clip-clop his horse up to the gate and blow his whistle. This was the night for Elmer Tuggle, Barney Google, and Skeezix. Ella Cinders and her brother endured horrible lives so bravely. I loved the smell of the newsprint, and even as I grew older and graduated to Dorothy Dix and editorials, there was always a remainder of the funny-paper excitement left, and I could smile at the Trio when they raced madly to get there first.

At the knock, Mama called: "Prilla, it's the paper boy, come for his money. It's right behind the mirror." I opened the door to find Mr. Simmons from the telegraph station. "This is for you, Prilla." His eyes were sad and I thought he was going to cry. I felt sorry for Mr. Simmons, having to deliver these telegrams, much too frequently. He didn't have a horse and he'd walked all the way across town.

I knew that Colton was dead. I gave the telegram, unopened, to Mama and went in to lie down on my bed and die, too. She offered Mr. Simmons a piece of pie and a glass of milk, but he refused. I heard the kitchen door protest as he opened it to leave.

Her hand was soft and gentle on my head as she stroked my hair. Papa came in to sit on the foot of the bed. He patted the sole of my shoe. They must have sat there an hour, maybe longer, and none of us could speak. Mama left the room and came back in with a glass of milk and two cookies. When I looked at them, I cried, as much for Mama and Papa, who couldn't comfort me, as for Colton at the bottom of the sea, and the unbuilt house and the unsewn curtains and the unpainted cradles and our unborn babies.

"We thank Thee for the light of this day and for the many blessings Thou hast seen fit to bestow upon us," prayed Papa. "Thank Thee for the lives of the boys Thou hast spared, and we ask Thee to bring them safely home to us. Give us, in these hours, the strength to bear our woes and keep our faith. We pray for the sick and the afflicted, the widow and the orphan, and for the Missionary abroad preaching the Gospel. Bless the President of the Church so that he may lead us and guide us according to Thy mind and will. And in a special manner, bless our dear Prilla Lou so that she"—his voice broke, and I sobbed into the chair where I knelt—"may fill the void in her heart. Give her work to do and strength to do it. Amen."

Well, Papa prayed well, as usual. The work came for all of us and we seemed to have abundant strength to do it. The flu came swirling into our town like a virulent tornado and as it swept through it took several lives. Papa was on call continually, to administer to the sick and to find men to help old Brother Allen with his gravedigging. In our family the Trio came down with it first, and Jeremy with his sensitive throat was terribly ill. We took turns sitting with him. Emily Ellen ran back and forth from the post office to the store and home. She always went three blocks out of her way so that she would not have to pass Johnny Winterrose's funeral parlor. Now there was always a light in the back and a buggy in front, it seemed. It took longer, but no one chided her.

Papa finally came down with it and then Mama. The twins came home from their work to help me nurse them.

The tornado swirled on downcountry and we survived

it. Ted Davis was killed in France, and his mother came crying to weep with Mama. We rolled bandages and knitted scarves and worried about Duncan and Clay, who were also in France. I think June and July wrote to them every day and they would get letters in bunches. They'd sort them out according to date and then start reading through every one swiftly, greedily, and then through them all again, slowly this time. When the letters came, my grief for Colton would come back with all its first sharpness and I would hurry out to mix bread, kneading it until my shoulders ached, my tears dripping onto the smooth dough.

But in November the torture ended, and the boys were coming home. The twins began once again to ready their much-readied trousseaus, to replace the dresses they had worn, to embroider and quilt and make white fruitcake.

Rollo came home first, and before June and July's weddings could be announced, Alice was expecting. Mama was so pleased. There would be another baby in the family. Alice was quietly beautiful and Rollo adored her. He was planning to build a house on the corner of our lot for her and our house began to take a glow of life again.

Tyler's third child, a son, had arrived and Papa beamed. He loved the two little girls, but here was another Woodrow to carry on the name. Tyler was happy over the baby, a robust, blue-eyed little fellow, but Tyler looked more gaunt and worn than he ever had. He never came home to visit, he was always too tired, and, caught up in a postwar tempo, Mama and Papa couldn't make it to Park City. It took nearly all day, for Papa still didn't hold with motorcars.

Rollo needed more money for his house, so he went to Silver City to work in the mine for the winter. Alice wasn't too strong, so he left her in Provo with her grandmother. The separation was to be for just a short while. He hated leaving her, but he wanted to get his walls around her, he said.

Papa was doing quite well. He'd bought some cattle and the small herd was thriving. Financially, he was on the threshold of security and he was pleased to know that Rollo would be living nearby to help out with the growing responsibilities. Davy was beginning to be a big help and Jeremy tried to be. If only Tyler looked better! Mama had come home shocked from her last trip over to Park City. Tyler hadn't worked for a while, and Margaret certainly was not able to get work, with a sick husband and three little children.

Papa hitched up the team and went to look things over. He brought Tyler and his family back, put Tyler to bed in the big north bedroom, and called the doctor. He'd found Margaret in debt and struggling bravely with bills and babies when he arrived, and I guess he knew that there was more than overwork and the airless mine wrong with Tyler.

Stretchable as it was, our house wasn't made for two families. Mama said that no roof was big enough, so Papa built a small three-room house at the top of the lot for Tyler and his family. It wasn't a fine house. But to build it and clear up Tyler's debts, Papa sold all his beef cattle. Tyler, when he could, helped with building the house. His skin was yellow and his chest caved in, but he and Papa were closer than they had ever been. Of the two, Papa seemed years younger; he moved with energy and zest and shook his head at night when he came in from putting in hours on the house.

"It is not well with Tyler, Kate. He is as weak as a kitten. As weak as a kitten."

The house went up fast. The High Priests' Quorum showed up one day to help; the next day it was the Elders'

Quorum. Sometimes the same men worked day after day, a few hours, to get the house built, and it seemed no time at all before Margaret and her children were moved in. Papa planted their garden and bought them a milk cow, which Davy milked for them night and morning.

With June and July's weddings over, it was peaceful. June and Clay decided that they had waited long enough and, with only an announcement on the afternoon of their leaving, dashed to Salt Lake to get married. But July said, differing for once in her life from their common thinking: "I've waited this long, I'm going to do it up brown." She had two wedding receptions. One at home and one at Duncan's home. Then, breaking all the rules of etiquette, but strengthening the bonds of love, she divided all her gifts with June.

I was helping her divide the gifts, as nearly as possible matching item for item to be sent on to June. "What would these people think? You giving your gifts away?"

"I expect the ones that know us very well won't be surprised. If you've noticed, everybody is extra generous. The people who don't know us won't ever know about it. And besides they don't know which of us they gave to, anyway. Like Mama says, 'What the eyes don't see, the heart won't grieve,' whatever that means. Besides, Prilla, I've never had anything that wasn't half June's anyway. Except Dunc" —she grinned at me—"and as big as he is, there isn't enough of him to share with anybody." She shook her head at the grandparents who looked gravely down upon us. "One alone," she sang huskily, sorting and piling, "to call my own. Poor Grandma Campbell!"

The summer went by. Tyler improved a little. He got out more and more. He milked his own cow and weeded his garden. He would walk down and sit on the porch and joke with me. He encouraged Jeremy to keep trying with his spelling. He laughed with Papa's roar when Jeremy was expelled from school for throwing a bottle of ink at Atty Wootten.

"You won't think it's so funny when it's your son that's expelled," fumed Mama. "I've never seen such a family for laughing at troubles. Let anyone fall down around here and break a leg, you'd think there was a circus. It'd be a mighty accomplishment in this family if you all learned to laugh at sensible things."

The laughter was coming back. Our house had never been without it for long. Marybeth and Jeanne, old enough to know better, sold their hard-boiled Easter eggs to the grocer for candy and they accomplished what I thought all along was a secret goal. They tickled Jeremy while he was trying to build them a swing. He fell off the limb of the tree and broke his other arm. He, sturdy soul, didn't tell. They knew he wouldn't.

Jeremy succumbed to a temptation that the rest of us, with some difficulty, had resisted. Grandma's folding bed stood in the living room. It was an imposing piece of furniture, carved with flowers and birds and topped with a gilt-trimmed mirror. When the bed came down, the legs magically lowered themselves from out of the ornate decoration at its top and it was unbelievably roomy and uncomfortable. What happened inside it when it folded up was a subject for frequent discussion, but only Jeremy was intrepid enough to climb inside the case when the bed was lowered and release the spring to bring it back up. I guess what happened to him was about what happens to the lady inside the box at the carvinal when all the swords are thrust in one side and out the other, apparently piercing her through and through. When she is in a certain position, the swords do not touch her. But poor Jeremy was a novice at the contortionist's art, and if Papa hadn't moved rapidly at Jeremy's first scream for help, our boy would have been a historical first—the first person to be guillotined by a folding bed.

We had some pretty girls in our family, but Marybeth was beautiful. She was chosen as the angel in all the plays that had angels, little boys walked her home from school, and she was quite reasonably vain about her looks.

"I am," she stated one Sunday morning, just as we were leaving for church, "the prettiest one in this whole family." Mama was aghast. To think that she had reared a vain child. "Pretty is as pretty does, miss," she said tartly, and gave Marybeth a thimble pie. Poor Marybeth was teased constantly. "That's enough time at the mirror for Marybeth," Mama would say. "She's so much prettier than the rest of us, she doesn't need it." It was the truth; I looked at Marybeth sometimes and wondered how one person could be made so marvelously. Jeremy was a handsome little fellow, but he was always finding a couple of extra feet to stumble over. Marybeth had grace as well as beauty.

"You're all growing up," Mama fretted. "We haven't a baby in the house."

"You've the grandchildren, Mama." I pointed out.

"Yes, but it's not the same. They visit a minute and then they run on home. I like to have little children in the house." Then she looked at me. "You're a nice girl, Prilla. Colton wasn't the only man in the world." But, kindly, she didn't go on, and it was something that I still did not want to bring out and look at very closely. The pain was still there.

[CHAPTER SIXTEEN]

In our little town, it was the people who were important. Each individual. When you walked down the street, you seldom saw a stranger. You spoke to everyone and you stopped frequently to chat and pass the time of day. Birth was exciting, marriage was a culmination of romance, with most of the adults in town well prepared for an announcement, even though it was ever a surprise to the participants, and death, at any age, was a parting and, thus, a tragedy. Any one of these events meant that you made your specialty, an iced-orange cake, a bowl of potato salad topped with egg daisies, a pan of flaky biscuits, or a casserole. There was a steady stream of neighbors walking in, all the way across town sometimes, to take their bit and congratulate or console. Whenever I see the Vital Statistics column in the paper, I am amazed that such wonders can be reduced to a line of type.

Though it meant sleeping on the floor, on one of Mama's straw tickings dragged in from the top of the granary, we welcomed company. No one minded tripling, since in our family we were already doubled, in bed, and many times we had one big bed stretching across each of the big-room floors. This made it possible to visit, even though we were bone weary, while we rested. I often wondered how the last person awake felt, listening to all the breathing. But though I tried to stay awake, I never managed to be the last one. As I drifted off, there was always someone talking, and when the next day I would try to get her to finish whatever she was telling when I succumbed, she could never remember the rest. I think our house must still be filled with unfinished thoughts hanging invisibly in the air.

I loved having Mama's brothers come. They sang and told stories and Mama sparkled with wit and gaiety. Ours was a kissing family, and I disliked the first greeting, when everyone made his affectionate rounds. Though I could not help ducking away from mustaches (Mama said that kissing a man without a mustache was like eating an egg without salt—give me unsalted eggs any time!), I tried to be there to greet folks when they first arrived. If you made a belated entrance, you were often overwhelmed.

Aunt Sally's kids were the most fun. They were always thinking up pranks, tunneling through the haystacks, playing kick-the-can, holding egg races or standing-on-one-leg contests. Of course, everyone tried again and again to lie on the footboard of Mama's bed. We sat around at night with one candle flickering giants and goblins onto the ceiling and told ghost stories. But there was none of that bloody bones and Ivory soap stuff for us. These were real ghost stories, with people who rose from the dead, or wraiths who walked in miserable repentance for their sins. Now was the time that the mystery of the Three Nephites was brought up and recounted. Nearly every family had a Three Nephite story. Erma Jensen told us of the old man who called on her one hot afternoon and slept exhausted in her kitchen rocker, after asking her to count his money. There was a small bag of gold pieces and some silver—really quite a fortune, two hundred dollars or more. When he awoke, she told him how much he had and gave him her husband's dinner. For this he thanked her and blessed her against the coming pestilence. In the epidemic of that year (1918), Erma's family was the only one in town that didn't get the flu.

Mama would tell guiltily about the man who cursed her. And all of us could verify her story. This particular old man, white-bearded and bent of back, was selling paper and envelopes and pencils. Mama used the most ready and easily understood excuse. "I haven't any money. I'd buy your nice paper, but I haven't any money."

He looked at her under beetling white brows and said: "Lady, you are telling me an untruth. Why don't you say 'I have money, but I do not want to spend it on your paper'?"

"But," Mama insisted, "I have no money."

"From this day on," the old man said, "whenever you need writing paper or pencils or stamps or envelopes, one of these things you will lack. And," he balefully compounded the curse, "you will never have enough money to buy them in supply!" We called this Kate's curse. What's more, this was one case where the sins of the father were visited on the children. I have written letters on used advertising, paper towels, pieces of wallpaper. I have become almost as ingenious as Mama was. I have had to make my own envelopes and never can I find a stamp. It is easier to give up letter writing, and for me the long-distance phone has been a lifeline. My friends, knowing my plight, are constantly giving me stationery and some of them have sent stamped return envelopes and paper along with their letters. I know now why Mama would stomp about in a rage, repenting her sin till the day she died. When you go to get the stuff, it has disappeared. Nobody's used it, nobody's moved it, nobody's ever even seen it. Kate's curse!

Company came from far and near. The ones that came from far, like Aunt Sally, from the Indian reservation at Fort Duchesne, made the trip worthwhile. It was usually for the entire winter, or the entire summer. The ones that came from near usually spent the night at least. Little Betsey Blackley, her black eyes and blue-black hair the only reminder that she was a half-breed Ute Indian, would walk the two blocks from her house to ours with her nightgown neatly tucked under her spotless white apron. Leaving her comfortable featherbed, she would sleep on the thin-mattressed cot, listening quietly as we talked and laughed. She seldom had anything to say, but we loved her because she was one of the faithful. All throughout Papa's Mission, Betsey sent him a dollar a month, and that was a dollar Mama didn't have to send, so it meant a length of cloth for one of us, a new dress, two union suits, or, even more welcome, a birthday cake with a gallon of root beer from Ad Averett's confectionery.

After Betsey had slipped away before breakfast, leaving her bed neatly made and not waking any of us, Mama would tell us about her.

"It's funny to think that Betsey is an Indian. Most of

them are not quite like her. She looks more like a Puritan than an Indian."

"Yes, Mama, how come Betsey lives in a house like we do? Most of them would rather live in tepees, wouldn't they?"

"Most of them," she would chide, "haven't had more than tepees, so they appreciate tepees. That is a nice thing to learn—appreciation."

"Tell us about Betsey," we would coax, and though we knew, it was a story as Mama told it and we were delighted to listen.

Betsey's mother, Prenettie, had been a rag-tag orphan who wandered into town in the wake of her tribe's seasonal migration. Uncle Joe James had picked her up and taken her home to his wives for kitchen help, and also because the child was a bag of bones and Uncle Joe couldn't stand anything to look hungry. His wives were plump, his children were cheerful, round-faced imps, his cattle and hogs were the fattest to be shipped out of the valley. Prenettie's thin, drawn face moved him to action. For a while she helped out with the housework and the children, and when her bones were rounded out with a bit of flesh—she never carried enough to really please him—he married her. They had four children, and the slender, wiry dark youngsters were in great contrast to their plump blond brothers and sisters.

Uncle Joe spent all his mealtimes urging second portions on Prenettie and her children, but no amount of high living could put flesh on bones whose ancestors had gone centuries without it.

"Aunt Prenettie had four children. Betsey was the only girl. She married Uncle Dan Blackley. And now he's dead and she lives alone."

"Where are her children?"

"Poor Betsey. Her little brown babies died. No matter how much she scrubbed and boiled everything and carefully fed them, the dreaded second summer killed them. They'd develop diarrhea and run a temperature, and so Betsey buried all four of her little ones, not too far from where Mary and John are lying."

"So then she was all alone?" This, to us, was the tragedy of tragedies. To be all alone. "Poor, poor Betsey!"

"Not quite. Her brother Ben's wife died leaving seven children, and Betsey moved into his house and mothered and reared them until they were grown and married. Then she moved back into her own little one-room house. All these years she had kept it clean and scrubbed and spent a few solitary hours a week among her own things."

"So, now, she's all alone?"

"Well, yes. But she visits."

"She can visit here every night if she likes. I like her." Jeremy was ever a man of convictions. "I like her even if the cat has got her tongue all the time."

But Betsey came only when no one else was visiting and at intervals of three or four months. Often, though, she would beckon to us as we passed her house and we would sit on her steps, scrubbed white and smooth with ashes, and eat huge, warm slabs of gingerbread frosted with thick butter frosting and drink buttermilk from scoured tin cups. It was the best buttermilk in town, bits of yellow flecked its whiteness, and somehow it had a sweetness that no other buttermilk has ever had.

We had an odd assortment of guests. Before Papa ever released a man—or, as on a couple of occasions, a woman—from his jail, he brought him home to eat royally at Mama's table. Drunkenness was the usual charge, and after the offender had sobered up and cleaned up, he became, for the length of a meal at least, a member of the family. Many of these guests, by the time they finished, and left carrying their next two or three meals in a flour sack, were on their way to becoming rehabilitated members of society. Papa constantly received thank-you letters from them, nearly always with a postscript: "And remember me to your fine family and especially your dear wife."

Once he brought home a woman who had been abandoned, drunk and weaving, on the Exchange Corner. She didn't have a coat and the winter's first snow was imminent. Mama gave Alma her old brown coat. She had a new piece of woolen goods that she had been planning for quite some time to make up for herself, but she had to stay home from church for two weeks until she had time, sewing at night, to make her new coat.

Aunt Margaret Wood gave Mama a strip of fur (meant for her own coat, but, happily, fur made her itch), enough to go all the way around the collar, and Mama showed it to us with a "now remember." "Now remember, you can't give anything away. If you give with a cheerful heart, it seems like it just comes right back with a dividend." Papa read it to us a little more poetically: "Cast thy bread upon the waters for thou shalt find it after many days."

I have thought that Mama had a touch of Godlike nobility in her character, especially when she offered her dessert to one of us, usually as a special reward, sometimes because we eyed it so. I've eaten her dessert and puzzled how she could bear to give it up and not give it a second glance. When she took in Clementine, I knew that she was, rightly, a woman a man would crawl on his hands and knees a thousand miles for.

Clementine stayed with us about eighteen months, and when she left, she was still company. I couldn't help but pity her, but I was glad when she was gone. Although she had put Mama to bed with heartbreak, had embarrassed and distressed all of us, Mama still kissed her good-bye affectionately and told her with sincerity that, if she ever needed a home, she had one.

Clementine was the daughter of a cousin of a cousin of Mama's. And you do not turn your back on your own kith and kin. I tried once to tell Mama that Clemmy was hardly kith or kin, but Mama glared at me and said, cutting me as only Mama could: "It is high to be a judge!"

Clementine burst in on a stormy night, much as Marybeth and Jeremy had, in a flurry of stuck kitchen door and snowflakes and bundles.

"I am," she said toothily, "Aunt Susie Richard's daughter, Aunt Kate. Mama died about three months ago, and Papa went on business to California. Aunt Jane Wellington [Mama's cousin] said she thought you'd like to have me visit you, especially as you and Mother were such friends when you were girls. Well, there just wasn't no place to go. Papa sold the house to pay for Mama's funeral, and Aunt Jane, you know, is down with the rheumatiz. You know that poor woman has to be turned with a sheet? So I came on up here."

The story won Mama's sympathy, Papa's hospitality, and Clementine a bedroom of her own. She got the bedroom because, guilty as we felt about mistreating another human being, none of us would share a bed with her. She was built like a yarn doll, a round head which narrowed and expanded to a round top which narrowed and expanded to a rounder bottom. Her legs were also divided into three lumps ending in pitifully deformed club feet. "Papa never made enough money to have them operated on!"

Clementine had about her a sickly, sweetish odor. But not from soap or perfume; she just smelled that way. Her voice was nasal and grated painfully. She was older than any of us and yet she seemed younger. She followed Mama around, love and affection on her face, and she repelled me. The repulsion I felt and the battle I fought with myself about feeling that way almost drove me away from home, except that I didn't have any Aunt Kate and Uncle Dave. In the summer I hid in the Magic Circle, and in the winter I spent as much time as possible at the library. I told the family I was writing a book. Mama told Clementine to leave me alone. "Authors must have their privacy!" I did write one poem, which I sold to the Relief Society magazine for three dollars, and Clementine's worshipful admiration made me feel like one of Papa's Pharisees who prayed in public places so that all men might admire their good works.

Somewhere, before she came to us, she had met two men who became interested in her. Both of them were made up of unmatched features and clothes. I never could tell which was which, although we had to turn the living room over to her to entertain them once a week. I usually left, and Papa did, too. He didn't say anything, but I didn't like the silly giggles that seeped from under the closed door into the kitchen.

It was only when Clementine, to please dear Aunt Kate, took it upon herself to wash Mama's wedding china that I found that the rest of the family, except of course Papa and Mama, felt the same way I did, and the shared dislike made my guilt evaporate. After a while I could look upon her with the charity she deserved.

No one had ever washed the wedding china. It could sit in the china closet, unused, with dust settling noticeably on it, but we were not allowed to touch it. When Mama finally found a free afternoon away from her machine and without the interested interference of the Trio, she would wash each piece with the affection she lavished on new babies and polish it to a gleaming shine. Then she would carefully replace it on the dusted shelves and lock it away until the next precious time.

The dishes were lovely. The plates were square with the corners cut out of them. They were thicker than any other china I have seen, except for the china in restaurants, but they were as translucent as the thinnest of her English bone cups. A delicate sheaf of wheat and tiny blossoms was painted on each piece and it was rimmed with gold, real gold, she said. I am sure that it was, for when they were stacked on the table, the pieces glowed. They were smooth to the touch, the smoothest things I have ever felt, and each of us had asked if we might have a piece or two for our own "when Mama was through with them." None of us would have thought to want all of it.

Mama was Relief Society teaching, doing her beat, as she called it. All of us were away from the house except Clementine, who offered to stay home and keep the fires burning. I don't really know what happened. But apparently Clementine had wanted to do Aunt Kate a real favor. She heated water, slowly and painfully, for she had to go outside with a brass bucket and carry it in to heat on the stove. It was difficult for her to carry much at a time, so she must have made two or three trips. Then, and this I will never understand, she piled the precious pieces on a tray, all of them! Maybe she thought it easier to carry the heavy tray once than to make several trips; she was incoherent when I questioned her. But she made it to the step-down into the kitchen and stumbled, the dishes clattering and crashing about her.

Emily Ellen and I had met on Coleman's Corner and we walked home together. Emily cried and made little "oohing" sounds when she saw what had happened. We didn't see the accident, but we heard it as we approached the kitchen door.

I was furious. I wanted to beat Clementine over her round, mushy head and scream at her, but I knew that if I let myself go, I wouldn't be able to stop. We got a box and carefully picked up all the pieces, knowing that Mama would never forgive us if we threw one little bit away, if there was a chance that she could mend them. Every piece except two of the lovely square plates was broken.

Mama came in as we were picking up the pieces. Clementine had hobbled over to the rocker and was watching us through her tears. When Mama came, Clemmy started blubbering again. Mama went white and she walked over and slapped me and then Emily Ellen. "How dare you! You've been told!"

"They didn't do it, Aunt Kate," bawled Clementine. "They didn't break them. I fell, I only meant to surprise you. I fell. See, I've cut my knee and cut my hand!" She showed her pudgy knee and extended her very small, very fat hand.

Mama sat down and took the hatpin out of her hair. "Poor Clementine!" she said. "Poor Clementine!" Can you imagine!

I guess Papa and Mama sat up nearly all night trying to see if they could piece the things together. Finally, when

Mama would allow herself to realize what the rest of us knew, that the pieces were shattered beyond even the most patient gluing, Papa helped her to bed.

In the night I heard Papa's low-voiced rumble comforting her. And how I loved him that he could appreciate this feminine disaster. Once he turned on the lamp and went to the kitchen for something, a glass of water perhaps.

Mama didn't get up the next day. "She's a little done in," Papa said. "Just make her a pretty tray and see if she feels like eating." She didn't. It was only when Papa took in her supper and fed her that she ate. And then she laughed a little. "You'd think I was a big boob, your papa doing this."

She stayed in bed two more days, saying, but not insisting, that she could get up, but Papa said now was as good a time as any for her to have a rest, and it wasn't often he could get her under his thumb. She didn't say anything more, ever, about her dishes, but I saw her crying a few days afterward when she was cleaning behind the woodbox. I'd found some delicate splinters when I cleaned, but I hadn't pulled the woodbox out. I guess some of them had fallen there, too.

Mama didn't change at all in her attitude toward Clemmy, but the rest of us indignantly, though gently, cursed Clementine for her lumpy stupidity and I found that all the rest of them resented her as much as I had. It made it a little easier to live with her, but I was glad when she decided to accept one of her suitors (the two of them had been mooning disgustingly over her on alternate weekends) and went off with no more than a two-hour engagement to get married. That's one of the real comforts of being alive. Things can change so fast, or we can hope that they can.

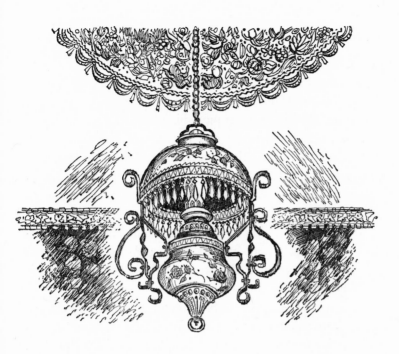

[CHAPTER SEVENTEEN]

Wʜᴇɴ ᴘᴇᴏᴘʟᴇ have nothing to say to each other, they talk about the weather. "Nice day, isn't it?" or "How is the weather suiting you?" or the those with a touch of originality say brightly: "Did you order all this rain?" But it goes deeper than that. The weather, to a great extent, controls our actions and, to an even greater extent, our deep thoughts and moods. "Happy is the bride the sun shines on," leaving a vast area for doubt and divorce for those who must accept, because of prior commitments, a gloomy day for their nuptials. A burial is not so terrible when the rays of the sun seem to dissipate grief and so, when storm and pain come simultaneously, both are worse somehow.

Disaster which came in winter was greater than the same

disaster in the summer, for winter immobilized us, shut us up in our houses, and limited our action to overcome it.

It was a cold day, a typical high-valley January Saturday. The snow had fallen and frozen and crusted over. It came almost as high as the fences. You stepped up from the porch and walked in a direct line across the fences to school or to town or wherever you were going, the sparkling snow crust tough enough to hold the weight of a man.

We had a fire going in the living room. Mama was darning in Grandma's high-backed rocker; Papa stood looking out the doorpane into the street. "My," he said, "what's bringing Aunt Rhoda out into this cold, with only a sweater thrown over her shoulders? She'll catch her death." Brisk, as I have known only her to be brisk, Rhoda Bennett pulled our gate back sharply through the snow and left it open as she hurried up the walk.

Papa opened the door.

"Uncle Dave! Oh, Uncle Dave! I hate to tell you. We got a call." (Aunt, by courtesy, Rhoda Bennett had the only telephone in our end of town now. Papa had ours taken out when he wasn't marshaling.) "It's Rollo. He's been hurt in a mine accident and they want you to get to Provo as fast as you can. I guess it's pretty bad."

"How was he hurt? Who called you?"

"He's in the hospital at Provo. The doctor called. Said they'd brought him in from Silver City just a bit before. I don't know anything more. Only they said you'd better hurry."

Papa could have asked Cy Olsen to drive him and Cy would have, but with the roads the way they were and danger of new snow and snowslides in the canyon, maybe they'd get there, maybe they wouldn't. Most likely they'd skid off one of the steep canyon sides. A horse and buggy, even as fast as Diamond still was, would be slower than if Papa waited until the Creeper plowed its way up the canyon and returned. We had about three hours before the train was due in town.

Mama went to get out Papa's Sunday suit, his Mission suit. She got out his valise and packed carefully folded white shirts, a change of underwear, clean stockings. She put in his Scriptures. Davy built up the fire and Emily Ellen and I filled the boiler so that water would heat for Papa's bath.

All the time that we were getting Papa ready, I wondered at Mama's calm. He had to shave and, though he'd shaved with his straight blade through all sorts of crises and prided himself on never a nick, he cut his chin and we had to find the alum to put on the cut to stop the bleeding.

We got out his heavy overcoat, and though his overshoes were worn and shabby he'd have to wear them in this snow. We'd gone together on his Christmas gift and given him a pair of fur-lined leather gloves. He hadn't worn them, but the Creeper was unheated and they'd be a boon now.

Mama packed him a lunch and dinner, headcheese sandwiches and one-egg cake. She put in a quart of peaches, too. He wouldn't get to Provo until nightfall and there'd be no place he could get a bite to eat.

Davy hitched the horse up and was waiting at the gate to take Papa to the station. Mama's chin trembled as she buried her face in Papa's overcoat. There had been no question about her going. Papa was no longer making his steady two dollars a day as marshal. He'd sold the beef and we lived on the milk and egg money. There was no money for two fares. And the Woodrows neither borrowed money nor ran their faces for goods.

"I'll call Rhoda and let you know how he is when I get there."

Taking turns sitting in Aunt Rhoda's kitchen, we waited that night and all the next day for the telephone to ring, but there was no call. We knew Papa had arrived because there was no storm, no word of snowslide, and the train came in on schedule. Mama sent Davy down to see.

"Ma, why doesn't he call?" There was no call.

The Trio slept, and finally Davy went to bed. Sitting up with Mama in the kitchen, I was lulled by the sound of the clock on its high shelf, the wood settling in the grate of the black stove, and the tiny efforts of the teakettle, set back off the fire, trying hard to whistle.

I heard a car door slam and I ran to open the front door. It was Papa and Dr. Baird, John Baird, one of Papa's boyhood chums, gone away to practice medicine years ago. They were helping Alice up the walk; seven months pregnant, pale, her usually high-piled hair falling around her shoulders, Alice did not look like anyone I had known before.

"The girl is in a bad way. Can we get her to bed?" When Alice saw Mama, she started to cry hysterically, and we knew that Rollo was dead.

Mama didn't cry and neither did I, but I wondered how my heart kept on beating when my chest felt so empty. We put Alice to bed, the doctor gave her something to drink. It was pretty powerful, she went right off to sleep. We went back into the kitchen to stoke up the stove and get Papa and Dr. John something to eat.

"I was there when they brought your boy in. I called Rhoda. His little wife, poor child, fainted when she got there and saw him, so we put her to bed. She's in no condition for such a shock."

Tyler, seeing figures moving through the light of the big kitchen window, had made his way down through the lot, leaning on Margaret's shoulder. The kitchen door protested as he pushed it open. "Why don't you fix this damn door sometime?" he asked angrily of no one in particular. "What is it, Pa? How bad is it?"

"He's dead. An accident. Something to do with the cage. It crushed him from the hips down."

"Oh, Dave, why didn't you call? It's been terrible."

"As long as you didn't hear, Kate, you could think he was alive. That's why I didn't call. He wasn't dead when I got there. He talked to me. He grinned." Papa raised his head high and took a breath and swallowed. "I had to wait until I knew something to tell you. They had operated. They took his legs off."

Mama covered her face with her apron, Tyler sat at the kitchen table and, with his arms and face lying flat against it, weakly cried, and I was there with my brother, my wonderful laughing brother, watching them take off the legs that ran errands, that delivered pins, that never, never carried him at a walk.

"Without his legs, he wouldn't have wanted to live," I said, and I knew that I spoke truly for him. He could not have borne a wheelchair.

"They were slow bringing him in from the mine," said Dr. Baird. "We could have saved him, I think, but he had lost too much blood. He'd have been a cripple. We did everything we could."

"I know you did, John, I know you did," consoled Mama. "Will ham and eggs be all right? It's about all there is in the cupboard right now." They sat at the table and ate, Papa looking out the window into the night so that he would not see the food he ate.

"This is the first I've eaten today," he said. "I thought Rollo was going to make it. I went out to get me a bite, but before I got through the outside door a nurse came after me.

"He said: 'Come over here, Pa. I think I'm slipping.' And he was gone. Twenty-five years old!" I had never seen Papa cry, and though he kept throwing his head back, oddly, as if to make room to swallow, he didn't cry now. I was glad that he didn't.

"Where is he now, Dave?"

"He's coming home on the train tomorrow. I took care of things before I left. I couldn't call you, Kate. I couldn't call you on that phone and tell you he was dead. I couldn't have borne it, telling you like that."

"It's all right," she said soothingly. "It's all right." I've heard her say the same words a hundred times in the years gone by. When the buggy tipped over on the way to the Campbell reunion, when Jeremy gashed his leg from knee to groin on barbed wire, when the babies cried from colic, it was "all right," and somehow the fear and pain left, and I knew that she comforted Papa now.

Papa had endured more heartbreak than we knew and it wasn't for a long time later that we found out. One of the undertakers, far more enterprising than our kindly Johnny Winterrose, had an arrangement with some of the hospital attendants. Rollo's body was whisked from his room and into a waiting carriage. Papa, numbed with shock, accepted the arrangement, and when he went to make further arrangements found that everything had been done for him. Rollo was dressed and ready to be shipped home in his casket. He would have accepted that, too, and paid the bill, except that he "thought that was an awful flimsy suit they'd put on him." He fingered a sleeve and was stunned to find that "to save money for the family of the bereaved," Rollo had been dressed in only the front of a suit, tied under the wrists and other places. The "saving" was concealed in the folds and puffs of his coffin.

I can imagine Papa's thunder-and-lightning indignation. "You take off that damned false rig and give me his body naked as he came into this world, you vulture," he roared, "I'll take him home where he can be dressed fitting. No son of mine is going to come forth in the morning of the First Resurrection with his backside sticking out!" The undertaker put the mutilated body in a wooden box and had it carted to the train. He did not argue over his lost customer and I can understand why, for Papa in a rage towered over men many inches taller than he.

Tyler insisted that he go with Papa and Davy and the twins' husbands to meet the train. Six of the men from the High Priests' Quorum were waiting for them when they got there. From the car they lifted the big wooden box that held Rollo's body and carried it to the wagon.

June and July had come from Salt Lake during the night. They had brought cakes and pies, salads and rolls. I knew what had happened. They had thrown themselves into a frenzy of busyness in order to endure the time until they could start for home. Aunt Rhoda had called them.

Now all of us waited at the gate as the wagon rolled in. But all they unloaded from the wagon was the big, queerly short wooden box. Papa had left Rollo at Johnny Winterrose's funeral parlor. They put the box in the granary. Something about it nagged at me and then I remembered: the box didn't have to be very long; a man without his legs isn't very tall.

Rollo's was the first loved one's funeral I had attended. Mama didn't encourage our attendance when we were small and we usually offered our services in some more helpful way. In those, actually few, bereavements of the friends I had known, we sat with the younger children, or straightened the house, or helped the Relief Society Sisters prepare lunch for the family and friends returning from the graveyard. Occasionally, the twins and I had sung at the funerals of babies or children, but we had known none of these well.

I do not remember much about Rollo's, except that I sat and suffered, trying to choke back sobs. With the music and the speakers evoking memories of him, making it almost unendurable, I thought that this was some sort of civilized torture rack that stretched the sufferer's soul far more agonizingly than any ancient barbaric one had stretched a body. There may be something to say for honoring the dead, but for me it cannot outweigh the horrors of putting mourning on exhibition.

Mama had quietly, but constantly, wept, mingling fresh tears with those of the friends and relatives that came to say good-bye to Rollo as he lay sleeping his last night and day in the splendor of the black, purple, and gold wallpapered parlor. Papa had spoken to them all in his strong voice, agreeing that Rollo, a cripple, was a far worse prospect than Rollo "out of this vale of tears."

Both of them had walked tearless and proud down the aisle behind his coffin. Papa supporting Alice, Mamma, little mama, supporting Tyler, the oldest son. I concentrated on the flowers, and on the patched place in the ceiling where Candida had fallen through. Looking at that, I had a freakish desire to laugh. What a shock that would have given old

Lizzie Jones, who was peering carefully at us as we walked. But Rollo might have laughed in such a situation, and even gossipy old Lizzie would recount it: "You know, not even a funeral can faze that second Woodrow boy. My, he is a jolly one. It does a body good to see a lad with a smile like that one!"

It was when they lowered the coffin into the grave that Papa started to tremble, and then he cried. Deep, tearing sobs that began low in his stomach and tore their way out of his throat. "My son," he said, "my dear boy, my son! O God, help me, I cannot let him go." I could not even put out my hand to comfort him as he had patted my foot the day that Colton died. His grief was a terrible thing for us. June and July turned to their husbands' arms, and Davy sobbed, his voice, just changing into a man's, only audible if you were as close as I was. The Trio, shocked and pale, huddled like chicks, close to me. Emily Ellen stood quietly, tears rolling down her cheeks.

Mama got up from her chair that someone had brought and thoughtfully placed for her at the graveside, and she took Papa's hand, as she would have led one of the grand-children, and seated him.

With her handkerchief she wiped his tears and put her hand, in greatest tenderness, on his cheek. Gently she stroked it from his temple to his chin. I had never seen her do that before, but she must have done it privately many times, for many years later, when she was gone, it was for the "touch of that little hand against my face" that Papa grieved.

Rollo had left a sizable amount of insurance and savings, and Alice, when she recovered from shock and pregnancy, was to find herself in what was considered, in our town, the enviable position of a beautiful, exciting, and wealthy young widow.

Papa girded up his loins, took fresh courage, and spent his considerable energies trying to help Tyler, advise and aid a surprisingly headstrong Alice, and make a living from the farm with the aid of only Davy and Jeremy. Davy was obviously unhappy on the farm, but Jeremy was very happy; he just wasn't very useful. Sent to put in a headgate for the watering turn, Jeremy could be depended on to turn the water into the wrong ditch, fall in it, step on a broken bottle, or get stung by a bee—or, as in Jeremy's case, bees, a whole hive of them.

But the day he smashed the chandelier was among his several worst. Optimistic, as usual, he was bent on sweeping a mouse out of a parlor corner. Somehow the broom was waved wildly in the air. I doubted, as Jeremy obviously did not, whether any mouse could jump so high. Suddenly there was a shattering crash and our parlor lamp, our glorious pride of many years, hung in tinkling shreds.

There was no punishment equal to this deed. Sometimes you just had to, as Mama quoted, "lay me down and bleed awhile, and rise, and fight again."

We sort of gave up trying to make a productive human being of Jeremy. He may have done things wrong, but he invariably did them funny, and Mama was always saying: "There's more room in this world for a laugh than a frown." We just allowed Jeremy to grow.

Since Rollo's death, Davy, depressed by Tyler's illness, was not ready for the workload that descended upon him. Papa, throwing himself into work as an analgesic, perhaps didn't consider that Davy was not yet grown enough to keep up with him. There was so much to do around the farm. If Jeremy milked a cow, it either held back her milk or kicked him somewhere, usually in the head. Mama, fearing that his brains might be addled, helped with the milking. I hadn't known that she knew how, but she got more milk, patiently stripping, than Papa ever did. This helped, for the creamery checks went up.

Alice had her baby in Provo, a girl, whom she named Rachel Ann, and as soon as she could travel, they moved in with us. There was room now, and we enjoyed the baby. Papa smothered his disappointment that Rollo hadn't left a son and he sang to her as he had sung to the rest of us. "Come over here, my son," he sang loudly and with vigor, and Rachel Ann chuckled and beamed at us with Rollo's smile.

Alice would curl up on the couch with a piece of fudge and a magazine and seemed oddly detached from the baby. She had decided against using some of her savings to build the house that Rollo had planned for her, though Papa and Mama urged her. She went out with many of the town's personable young men, and then, bored, she left Rachel Ann with us while she went to work in Salt Lake City.

Davy, maybe because he had loved Rollo so, devoted a lot of time to the baby. He taught her to walk, standing her firmly on her white-shod feet (Alice dressed her baby beautifully), and coaxed her to take just one more step for Uncle Dave. He'd put her, fat legs sticking straight out, in front of him on the saddle and walk his horse round and round the barnyard, grinning in delight at her enjoyment. She was a nice baby. Cheerful and healthy and responsive. She'd cuddle against you lovingly and pat your shoulder with rhythmic affection.

Davy was teaching her to talk. "Say 'Dave.' Say 'Un-cle

Dave,' " he'd coax. "Come on, honey, say 'Un-cle Da-ave.' "
"Wacho," she'd chortle. "Wacho, Wacho, Wacho."

"See," he interpreted, "she can say her own name. She's just stubborn."

Maybe if Alice hadn't popped in one night with a slender, dark-haired, serious young man named Adam Wells and introduced him as her new husband, who was here with her to take Rachel Ann home, Papa wouldn't have lost another son. Who knows? (Nothing can leave behind as much emptiness as a baby.) Just a week after Alice took Rachel away, crowing and laughing and blowing kisses to us, Davy packed up his things and swiped a suitcase which was Tyler's and left. He wrote back later that he hadn't really stolen the suitcase, he'd send it back if Tyler wanted, but he figured, and rightly, that Tyler would never use it.

Like Tyler, he strapped himself to the top of a freight car and rode it, but he didn't stop in Nevada. He rode right on through, and, tired of the plow and the brown earth clods and the "walk a mile this away, walk a mile that" area of our town, he found a different, wider world. He joined the Navy.

Davy had inherited Kate's curse. So two letters a year were about all that he wrote. Entranced with California's citrus wonders, he sent us, as a peace offering, a crate of oranges and lemons with the freight, C.O.D. The freight on that fruit was $17.10 and Papa thunder-and-lightninged for two weeks. So they wouldn't spoil, he ate the oranges and then the lemons, noisily and suffering, and vowed if he had Davy near enough, he'd thunder-and-lightning wish he wasn't.

Tyler had gradually slipped backward again after his

slight improvement. He was bedfast now, and his medicine cost twenty-five dollars a bottle. That twenty-five dollars would keep Tyler almost comfortable for two weeks or so. For the first time in all my life I heard Papa fret about "getting hold of a few dollars." I was making enough clerking in the Merc store and writing little squibs from the county for the *Deseret News* to pay for my salt, but that was about all. I don't know how Davy found out—I guess one of the twins wrote him—but though he didn't write, every two weeks there'd be a money order in the mail for Papa, and Tyler was assured his medicine.

The summer stretched on, unusually hot for a mountain summer. The breeze couldn't seem to find its way into the bedroom where Tyler was trying to die. He tried hard and it took him all summer long. At nights after the chores, Papa and Mama walked up through the lot. Watching them through the kitchen window, I noticed that Papa's shoulders were bent a bit. Mama couldn't have grown, but she came almost even with his shoulder. Maybe it was a trick of the twilight or dread of the night's vigil. They sat with Margaret night after night, dozing a little in their rocking chairs which Jeremy had carried up for them. It was Jeremy's thought to do this, and I thought it boded well for the future, since, as far as I knew, it was his first constructive action.

Then one morning Tyler dropped into a sound sleep, the first deep refreshing sleep he'd had in weeks and weeks. It must have been wonderful, for Tyler refused to waken and he slept the clock round again. I paid my short daily visit, taking a pitcher of lemonade, and ice that I had borrowed, though Papa didn't approve, for Tyler enjoyed it. Gaunt and yellow, his face on the pillow was the face of a stranger and the skeleton of his tall body showed where the sheet lay on him.

"He's surely sound asleep, poor boy," Mama whispered.

"Yes, Kate. Thank God. He's gone to sleep. He's dead, darlin'."

Papa had known he was dead for quite a few minutes, but he was gathering strength to tell us.

Tyler was my brother and I loved him and I honored him, but I could not go to his funeral, and so I pretended that Rachel Ann (Alice had come home to pay her respects) would be unhappy among strangers, and no one thought to tell me I was not honoring my dead.

Lizzie Jones paused in front of Tyler's coffin, placed as Rollo's had been placed, the exact angle, the same lace-shaded lamp, the same bit of transparent veiling over the top half of the casket, its pink unsuccessfully trying to hide Tyler's terrible jaundice.

"My, doesn't he look natural?" She clasped her hands in front of her little potbelly and watched me with the beady, snoopy eye of a chicken. "Prill, I'd a known him any-where!"

Behind me I could have sworn that I heard Tyler's deep amused chuckle and the infectious roar of Rollo's laugh. I almost turned to see them sitting on the floor, clutching their middles in unholy glee.

"Yes, real natural," I said, and looked back at them warn-ingly. But they had gone.

[CHAPTER EIGHTEEN]

I CAME home from the store early one fall afternoon.
Brother Selby's mother had died and he closed up so that all
of us could attend the funeral and pay our respects. Old
Sister Selby had been bedridden for years. She scarcely recognized her own family, let alone a visitor, and I had never
seen her that I remember, since the Selbys lived in the Second Ward. Even in a town as small as ours, the scope of life
was narrowed to the confines of the Ward. It was only after
you had passed through the Central School that you mingled
with the students from the North School, for the products
of both were channeled into the County High School. It was
then that you branched out and got to know people outside
the circle of your relatives, and by the time you graduated
and married, in one way or another you knew everyone in
town. Of course, Papa and Mama knew everyone because

they had grown up with the town, or perhaps it was the other way around.

Fall was my time of year in our valley, especially if winter tarried a bit and the long, crisp, Jonathan-apple days could linger. On my way home this day I met no one. The street was unusually empty. Even the blacksmith shop sent only the acrid odor of pared horses' hooves and hot iron onto the street. Bill John had closed up to attend the funeral and the usual sounds of pounding horseshoes and men visiting were absent. I always thought that Bill John's bellow of joy when he heard a story, some of them over and over again I am sure, brought more customers than his neat hand with a horseshoe. You could hear his laugh sometimes over the rolling of the wheels and the clop of the horses hooves on the street when you started up his block.

I walked slowly, savoring my world and thinking that maybe just to see the blue of an optimistic sky that doubted the ability of any cloud to climb high enough to get over our mountains was wonder enough for one day. Maybe old Sister Selby had loved this world as Papa did and as I was beginning to. And if you loved something enough, you could die for it quite peacefully. Though there were times when I wondered and would wonder again, at that moment, just seeing and smelling and hearing was enough. Living was certainly worth dying for.

Lucy Cliff's everbloomers were beautifully outdoing one another to see which could bear the last rose of summer, and I stopped to lean on her picket fence and look at them. I knew that, early that morning, she'd been out to pick the largest and loveliest ones for a bouquet to send over to the Selbys. I guessed that being able to do that was part of the reason why she was up before sunup working in her garden. Lucy was genteel. None of the women of her family had soiled their hands doing common work. She was one of the ladies Mama sewed for, but she worked like everyone else in town, whether or not they could afford a girl. She just did it when she thought no one would know about it. Her flowers always took first place in the Fair and she'd accept the blue ribbon with the same little smile and a thank you to her boys and husband for being such wonderful gardeners. When Lucy died, her secret came out, for her garden died with her.

"Why's Mrs. Cliff ashamed of honest work?" Jeremy asked Papa. "I asked her what she used to get the bugs off her roses and she acted like she was mad at me. Said to ask Mr. Cliff, if I could catch him to home. Said she thought he used soapsuds and washed them off. Gollee, Papa, Mr. Cliff don't even use soapsuds on his hands. She said if I used the soapsuds, like Mr. Cliff did, to wash the roses off careful again. Now, just why's she ashamed of honest work?"

Papa shook his head. "What she thinks is none of our affair, Jeremy. It's what she does that counts. And there's not a house in town, I'd say, that hasn't had a bowl of Lucy's roses some time or another. Learn to accept folks, son, it makes everything simpler."

I thought of that as I leaned over Lucy's fence and stole a pink bud, a thing I would not have dared to do if I hadn't known that she was gone.

The Central School took only one part of the large block set aside for it and through the center of the block, cutting it into defined triangles, was a path beaten by the feet of the residents of the southeast part of town. Now, on both sides, the sunflowers had grown up and weeds flourished. When school started again, there'd be Clean-up Day and the students would rake and hoe and bring box lunches, though all of them were within lunch-hour reach of home. The principal would ladle out punch from a tub weighted down with a miniature iceberg, and Clean-up Day was a holiday. Then, once again, the school grounds would be smooth and free of weeds and dusty until the snow fell. In the winter sometimes the snow would be two feet deep or more on each side of the cutoff. The snow plow would clear this path as it did the sidewalks. I guess the path had saved countless hours of time, if such savings could be totaled.

Once you had crossed the school grounds it was a block to Coleman's Corner and then you could see our house. I loved seeing our house. It welcomed you. In the summer the trees bent toward you and in the winter there was smoke beckoning from the chimney, giving the place the look of a Christmas card. You know the kind, with the sparkles, sprinkled crusty and rough to your fingers, over the trees and roofs. Always at night there was a light in the parlor window so that you could see it when you rounded the corner. Before we had street lights that was quite a comfort, especially if you'd run breathlessly through the school lot with goblins chasing you all the way.

Now as I walked I felt that welling of warmth that I always felt. Sometimes Mama would be standing in the door watching for you, if you'd been sent on an errand. "My, but you're slow. I could have gone twice and back in this time." She could have, too.

Often, almost as if he were waiting for us to come home from school (I've never thought about that before, but I guess that was really what he was doing), Papa would be weeding or clipping the lawn or fixing the fence as we rounded the corner. Then, when we arrived, his chores on that side of the house were suddenly done and he'd go on to the barnyard.

Inside, the cool would be wonderful after walking through the heat, and if you'd plodded through the snow, always high enough to get down inside your boots, the warmth of the kitchen, once you'd bunted the door open, welcomed you. Mama usually had hot cocoa and the oven door was down with sticks of wood across it so that you could sit around and put your feet up on them to get them warm.

The house I always loved, but it took a while—not until I grew older and tall enough to see over the fence—for me to realize how beautiful was our valley and how beautiful was our world!

Unlike many towns and cities, I've found, when you came into our town, no matter from which direction, you approached by way of hills and streams and fields. The mountains rimmed the valley and no matter which way you looked they reached skyward, sometimes gentle and rounded, sometimes spiking sharply upward. But always they were protective. When Papa read to us, if he read long enough, he'd always get around to the Last Days.

"And in the Last Days the people shall flee to the valleys of the mountains." The Last Days held no terror for us, for we were already sheltered in the valleys of the mountains and we could fear no evil.

Sometimes you can pinpoint the days when you did some growing up. I think the walk home on the day of Sister Selby's funeral was one of those times for me. I suddenly felt something inside me expanding—my soul, Papa would have said—and for the first time since Colton's death had shut me inside myself, I felt that deep, snuggle-in-a-featherbed contentment, which is probably the nearest thing to happiness.

I walked along the grassy sidewalk toward home and smelled the camomile as I crushed it under my feet and was glad that I was grown enough to refuse it when Mama brewed it up as tea and gave it to us for what ailed us.

The squeak of the gate as I pulled it open was a dear and friendly sound, and the curve of the cement walk, which Papa had poured himself, drew me around past the prickly pears and bachelor's buttons, past Papa's little ponderosa pine he'd cradled all the way home from the hills, past thick green beds that yielded buttercups for golden bouquets to put on the babies' graves each spring, past the morning glories that covered the south side of the house, past the cellar door, open now. Someone was down there, probably Mama, choosing a spring-canned jam for supper or fruit for a pie.

I felt the rough places in the cement underneath my soles, where Papa had patched the original work, and I put my hand on the warm white wood of the corner of the house. I loved the house and I loved whatever I would find inside when I opened the door.

[CHAPTER NINETEEN]

My family portrait," Papa said, "never got taken." I was riding with him to the canyon to get wood. While I wasn't much help, I could sit on the logs as he sawed, and drive the team along after him when he loaded on the logs, smaller ones than when Tyler and Rollo could go with him to help. It was on this trip that Papa told me about his imagined family picture.

"When the boys were here, we couldn't afford to have old man Willis take the picture, and now it's too late. Folks shouldn't put off." He shook his head. "They just shouldn't put off. It'd be a family mostly of girls." But he smiled at me gently. "Finer girls, though, you'd not find in a far piece."

We passed Will Masters's place, tucked down in a wrinkle between two slopes of the foothills.

"Now take Will's daughter. I guess she was what killed Aunt Mary Masters, and the shock of Aunt Mary's death took Will off sooner than he shoulda gone. I tell you, Prilla, I'd sooner see a daughter of mine dead than drunk!"

I was surprised by Papa's vehemence and I wondered, too, if he felt that way about his sons. I remembered Mama putting Rollo and Ted to bed after the bout in Park City.

"That girl in there. Ever seen her?" He jerked his head back to the gray house we'd just passed.

"No. The only time I've ever been up here, before, was with some kids looking for chokecherries. They said she was a witch and we didn't go close. Does she drink, Papa?"

"It's sad. Wasteful. Sad. She played the violin. Real good. I guess she was just about the only genius ever came from these parts. Her folks sent her back to New York to school and then to Paris and Vienna, I think it was. She could make that old fiddle sing and cry, dangdest thing you ever heard. She played in church one time, before she went to Europe. I've never heard music like that before nor since. She traveled all around the world and even played for George the Fifth, I heard. I don't know. You know how folks sometimes get carried away in what they say. Anyway, I know she made lots of money and sent a deal of it home to her folks, too. Paid them back for sending her to school. They had a new buggy and Mama made her a new dress practically every month or so. Fine people. Had a right to be proud. Then Eleanor, that's the daughter's name, met some married feller and he got a divorce over her."

Papa looked at me to see how I was taking his revelation of the seamier side of life and continued: "She didn't marry him, though. She got to livin' high and drinkin' and the next thing we knew, her Pa was meetin' her on the train. She came out here with him and never has come in to town that I know of, 'cept once. I picked her up after midnight, one night, drunk, and cryin', and wet from fallin' in the snow. It was right after her mother died. I took her home before it was light and folks could see Will's shame.

"Will told me she said she'd kill herself if he didn't let her have her whiskey. Maybe he should have let her go ahead. It killed Mary and him, that's for sure. They never came to a meeting after she came back to the valley."

"Oh, Papa, that's sad. The poor thing."

"Yes," he said, "I guess it's sad. Eleanor will die one of these days and the hired man she pays to look after things and buy her whiskey will move on with all her valuables, providing she's got any left."

Papa hadn't been a marshal for all those years without getting to know about people. That is almost exactly what happened to Eleanor, except that the hired man stopped by Johnny Winterrose's to tell him that Eleanor was dead and to leave an envelope with enough money in it to pay for her burial. The house was stripped, I heard, but there was no one to mourn Eleanor. She was the last of the Masters line.

"If there's anything left, which I doubt," I heard the sheriff telling Mr. Selby in the store, "let the man have it."

We passed the Masters place and Papa fell silent.

"Do you feel as strongly about your sons getting drunk?" I asked him.

"Strong drink is not good for man," he quoted.

"But do you feel the same?"

"It's worse, somehow, for a woman. Oh, I know, miss. I surmised your brothers took a nip once in a while, but they were good boys all the same. And I really don't know for sure. If I'd a caught them drunk," he added, "I'd a had to haul them into jail. I'm glad I didn't catch them."

He clucked to the horses and told me that just over that rise was where Molly Davis came face to face with a black bear while she was picking berries.

"Like to scared her to death," he chuckled. "But that bear was a sight more scared. That was one bear that went over the mountain 'cause he was frightened by a yellin' woman. Lots of men," he added, "have gone the same way for the same reason."

"You've still got quite a family, Papa, if you were to have a family portrait taken."

"Yes, but Tyler is gone, Rollo gone, Boot gone. Davy might never come back home again. I wouldn't have the heart now. Maybe later when the gaps have filled in more. Have you noticed how Tyler's little William looks like his daddy? I thought I'd have a great family of sons to pass on the Woodrow name, but there's only Davy and little William now. Sometimes the Lord just doesn't see fit to give a man the thing he wants the most."

"What about Jeremy?" I was surprised. Jeremy was my brother, as much as Davy.

"I love Jeremy the same as all of you, of course," said Papa gently. "But you can't get around it, Prilla, he doesn't bear my name."

That Marybeth and Jeremy would wonder about this was understandable, but I hadn't thought that they had, until one night when Mama was making out family group sheets.

"Where are we, Mama? You've left us out!" Marybeth had been copying Mama's work sheets in her neat handwriting. "Here's from July all the way down to Jeanne, but you've forgotten us."

Papa lifted his head from his paper and looked at her.

"Come over here, daughter," he said. He pulled her up on his knee. "Families belong together. Sometimes they have to be parted in this world, but in the next world families will be together. Your mother and daddy—you know, Uucle Jason is your real daddy" (Marybeth was aware of this but she called her father Uncle Jason, along with the rest of us), "were married for time and eternity, and so for time and eternity all the children they would have here on earth will be theirs in heaven, too."

"But this is my family," Marybeth said, bewildered.

"Of course it's your family," Papa said. "But you wouldn't want your mother and father to go through all eternity without any family at all, would you, when they love you just as much as we do?"

"Well, no!" Marybeth was extremely doubtful.

"So we've borrowed you for this life, but in the next you'll belong to them. Mama is going to make out a sheet for you and Jeremy and your father and mother so that you'll have a record, too."

"I don't think I like it that way, Papa," said Marybeth. "What are you going to do about it?"

Papa laughed. "Nothing right now. We don't have to. Now you belong to us the same as the twins and Jeanne and Davy and the rest." Marybeth was not content.

"How about if we all lived in the same mansion in heaven?" she asked.

"How about right across the street?" Mama interrupted quickly.

"Well, all right. Right across the street." Marybeth, her

problem for this life and eternity solved, hopped down from Papa's knee to continue her copying.

It was not so easy with Jeremy. Now he was the only son, and Papa, seeing him as that, tried to mold him into the Woodrow image. Where Rollo and Davy had been quick-moving and swift-learning, Jeremy was slow. Where Tyler had been thoughtful and accurate, Jeremy was heedless and awkward. Tyler was a tall man but he was slender; Jeremy was going to be a massive one. The Woodrow boys were impatient and inventive; Jeremy was patient and persistent. Papa's suggestions to his other sons were accepted, perhaps resentfully, but accepted. His wisdom acknowledged. Jeremy, while respectful, had to know why Papa was right, if he was right, and how he knew so surely he was right. Jeremy stubbornly refused the mold.

I had thought that Tyler's illness and Rollo's accident were trials enough and that three deaths were tragedy enough. I was to learn that these things are to be expected and accepted and that such grief is a wound that heals cleanly—slowly perhaps, but without disfiguring scars and colloids. We weren't to escape the suffering that comes with shame, the kind of suffering that pushed Mary and Will Masters into their graves.

Alice had taken Rachel Ann and moved into the home that Adam Wells had built for her. Adam was a good man and he brought Alice and Rachel Ann up to see us in their new Model T. If Rollo's money helped to pay for the house and the car, it didn't seem important, for Adam was affectionate with our baby and she hugged her Adam tightly when he lifted her up. I guess Adam might have been too good to Alice. Rollo's fire and wit and masculine demands would have kept her at his side, I am sure, but Adam had none of these and Alice was bored and suing for divorce within six months.

The quick maturity forced on her by Rollo's death and Rachel Ann's birth had made Alice an exceptionally beautiful woman. Now she had become aware that men turned as she passed by, and she made the most of it.

This was the first divorce in our family and we were shamed by it, for Alice was Rollo's wife and her resting place, if she wanted it, Papa said, was there in the family plot. "She's the only wife he'll ever have, and as long as she wants it, she'll have a home and a place with us."

That divorce was only the first. Dr. John told us wearily on one of his rare trips up home that he had evidence that Alice was living quite a high life. Then, one evening, the paper carried the story of a nasty divorce scandal. An embittered wife, after attempting to kill her husband, had named Alice as corespondent in the divorce action. Though the story was on a back page and only the people who knew us would know Alice Woodrow, the whole town knew us.

Mama wept and Papa burned the paper before I could read it, but everyone knew, although charitably no one mentioned it. We worried most for Rachel Ann, and her welfare was the "special manner" topic of our prayers.

Papa made one of his rare trips to Salt Lake, where Alice had moved. After two days of searching for her, he found that she'd married, the neighbors thought, and gone to California, taking our baby with her.

"She's Alice's baby, too, Papa. She's not going to allow any harm to come to her. Alice has always been a good little mother." I couldn't convince them and I knew why. They'd seen Alice ignore Rachel Ann when she cried for attention. But we had made little of it, since there were so many of us who loved to take care of the baby. Now I thought of my brother and his love for children and the care he took of us. He'd have adored that little girl. I worried now because Alice had been willing to leave Rachel Ann with us the first few months. If it had been Colton's child, I could not have borne to have been apart from her. We knew that Alice had plenty of money, though, and could afford care for Rachel Ann if she did not want to be herself burdened with the child.

But it is the immediate that gets the most attention. "The wheel that squeaks the loudest is the wheel that gets the grease," Mama put it. Suddenly we were caught up in preparations for Emily's wedding; Papa had finally approved her young man. June and July were both expecting their firstborn. Tyler's children ran in and out of the house, and Rachel Ann, so far away, was not squeaking very loudly, although she was always included in Papa's "and we place into Thy kind care and keeping our son Davy abroad on Thy infinite ocean and little Rachel Ann who is gone so far from us."

Dyke Palmer brought his three motherless little ones back home to his mother to care for and moved his dental office into a suite of rooms above the bank. Dyke had left right after high-school graduation to learn to be a dentist and had married a southern Utah girl I had never met.

I was just passing the door leading upstairs to his office when his littlest one, Sue Jean, spilled abruptly and painfully through it. I'd picked her up and was comforting her when Dyke came out of his office in answer to her high wail.

"You're still the same, Prilla. You don't look a day older than when we were in high school."

That was a stupid sentence to make my heart beat fast.

Not since Colton had I felt any pull toward a man, but now I did, and, flustered, I brushed off my skirt and tidied my hair.

"She's all right," I said. "Just a little bruised pride, I think."

Before Sue Jean had completely recovered her equilibrium and I my poise, Dyke asked me if I'd like to attend the band concert that night, and I accepted. It was that sudden and exciting. When he drove up to our gate and helped me over the ditch onto the sidewalk in front of our house, we both knew that this was more than a reacquaintance or a summer flirtation. And it only made me chuckle to think that Lizzie Jones would say, and maybe did, that finally Prilla Lou Woodrow had managed to avoid being buried an old maid. Nor did I feel that Dyke was looking for a mother for his youngsters. This was another Colton thing, mature and lasting.

But I did wonder what kind of a mother I would make for another woman's children and I was down-on-my-knees grateful for Mama. I knew that a Woodrow woman could not be the mother of another woman's children. They would belong to me.

So it was with joyousness that I welcomed Dyke into that "all others keep out" place in my heart.

[CHAPTER TWENTY]

Wealth, time, and age are among many other states that are relative. A blanket, a beef, and a box of matches would mean unimaginable wealth to an aborigine. Time, to anyone old enough to visit the dentist, can be endless or brief, depending on which side of the operating-room door he's sitting, and age can mean either that a person is old or that he is not.

Papa had a quality of interest and of excitement that he brought to living as long as he breathed. Each morning was a new day to be grateful for and enjoyed. "We thank Thee for the light of this day" was his morning prayer. If his love of living could have been dimmed, it would have been the winter of his operation. If we could have known a "poor" year, it would have been that year. But that year I discovered that "poor" and "rich" are, like many other things, perhaps just a state of mind.

None of us ever thought that we were poor; we had gone through life thinking blissfully that of all the world's families we were among those most richly blessed. Perhaps we could have felt poor the winter of Papa's operation. I remember that the Stake Presidency called on Papa one evening after he was enthroned in the living room as Grandma had been. The operation, for hernia, had been done under a local anaesthetic and somehow Papa's right leg was left cold, lifeless, and useless. It never occurred to any of us that our daily prayers that he would walk again would not be answered, but with all the Lord had to get around to, sometimes He took a little time.

"Brother Dave," through the half-opened door I heard. Such a delegation was not common and it was obvious that they had something important on their minds. "Well, it's like this. We know that you've been out of work and had a lot of expense with your illness and all. You've helped the sick and afflicted all your life and you're a hundred per cent tithe payer. It isn't charity we're offering, and you mustn't think it so, but it's money you've earned by righteous living that we want to give you now to tide you over this barren spot." I was surprised, and concerned, and then soothed again at Papa's answer.

"We don't need your money, but I thank you for the spirit in which you have offered it."

"Now, Dave, don't let false pride . . ."

"It's not false pride," Papa said surely. "We've all our property free and clear. We don't owe any man a dime. Our cellar is full of food and we've a little put by in the bank. Kate is a fine manager and there's so many needy in the town I'd be ashamed to touch a cent of church money."

Mama agreed when he discussed it later. "It was mighty nice of them to offer, but we'll get along fine." And we did.

That winter, which could have been poor, was our richest one. Papa picked up a tin flute that someone had given one of the grandchildren and he learned to play it. I played the piano. Jeremy played the drums. If we were not as good as the martial band that woke us up early on the Fourth of July, we weren't aware of that, either.

Every day of that winter was a holiday, for while usually we saved the use of the living room, and the extra wood it took to build a fire in the potbellied stove, for Sunday nights and other special occasions, with Papa in bed there, we used the room every night. People came to call and brought him treats, which he shared generously. We popped corn and read books aloud, taking a chapter apiece. And we sang.

Papa sat propped up and painted the little wooden doll beds that Mama and I built of Ad Averett's cigar boxes for Christmas presents for the grandchildren. He read aloud, and discussed everyone's church-history lessons, and the Trio got A's without turning a page. He told us stories of the valley that he'd never had time for before, and he read from the Bible and predicted another great war. "In the long run," he told us, "it'll be the Rooshiuns we'll have to watch. It's been prophesied that in the Last Days the Constitution, in other words the Nation, shall hang by a thread."

"Mama better not be around then. She can't stand to see a hanging thread. She'd bite it off." Jeremy looked around for approval of his wit. "Then all the prophecies would come true because, with the thread bitten into, the world would go zooming down through space and it'd catch fire like a meteor and burn to a crisp. Now, Pa, how else is this whole world gonna be destroyed by fire like you say it's gonna be?"

Papa silenced him with his preacher's frown and sincerity, picking up where he'd been interrupted. "And then the Elders of the Church will labor mightily to save the Nation."

We'd heard this many times before, but we went along with the proper responses.

"You mean a Mormon will be President?"

"That's most likely what it would have to be."

"How we gonna do that? There's gonna have to be a lot more Mormons than there is now to get all that many votes." Jeremy had been studying civics.

"With all the pestilences, and bombs and mustard gas left over from the war, I guess we could possibly have a war that'd wipe everybody out except those that 'flee to the tops of the mountains.' " Jeanne was always practical.

"There'll be another war," Papa said quietly. "Peace has been taken from the earth. There may be more than one war, and if the Nation is to survive, it must turn to God."

"Well," said Jeremy, "this is the great land of equal opportunity. You may be looking at the President of the United States right now—the Mormon one. A Mormon boy," he yodeled. "I am a Mormon boy! I might be envied by a king." His voice rose triumphantly. "I am a Mormon boy!"

"All right, Morman boy, go out and fill the woodbox— to the top. This stove burns wood faster than the kitchen stove does. It seems to, anyway. I hope we'll have enough stove wood to last the winter out." Papa worried, and the present superseded the past and the future. It was a good thing. It is much simpler to worry about a load of wood than the sun darkening, the moon turning to blood, nation warring against nation and brother against brother—much simpler.

But Jeremy's declaration of candidacy for the first Mormon President was slowed down a little by the next afternoon. He came home crushed at losing a school election.

"There were two of us in the finals," he said, "John Payne and me. The cheat! In the final vote, I voted for him and he voted for himself, and he won by one vote."

Papa threw back his head and slapped his lifeless knee in glee. "That's the first lesson of politics, my boy. Vote for the man you think is best or you can well wind up getting second choice." That brought up a new subject for games and all of us learned the Presidents, Vice-Presidents, their years of office, and their party.

"How come you're such a staunch Democrat?" we asked Papa, and he answered with a hint of a grin.

"It was like this. Because most of the people in the state were members of the Church and they were all of one mind, it was playing hob with the two-party system. So one of the Authorities made a trip out here. Everybody of voting age was asked to go to the Stake House for this important meeting and everybody went. Brother Kimball explained how the two-party system was the best way of checks and balances and how we were all voting the same way. He said: 'Now I'm going to divide this building right down the middle. The people on the left side of the center pillars are Democrats and the people on the right side of them are Republicans.' And," said Papa, "I've been a staunch Democrat ever since." When I think it over, that seems as good a reason as many I've heard put forth since.

Papa suffered with his leg, I know, for I heard him groaning in the night and I could hear Mama going in and out of the kitchen to get water for his pills. Sometimes I heard the murmur of their voices in the early hours of the morning, but he was always cheerful when we were about.

That winter marked Jeremy's growing up. He had to chop the wood now, for with fires in both stoves most of the time and no big-boy tempers to work off, the woodpile dwindled alarmingly. As soon as supper was over, we allowed the fire in the kitchen stove to die out and moved into the living room. Jeremy had to milk the cows, too. I was conscience-driven to learn one evening and he manfully pushed me away from the corral gate.

"The corral is no place for a lady, Prilla," he told me, and I was feminine and allowed this male to talk me out of something I didn't want to do.

With Jeremy's natural aptitudes, he must have had quite a struggle. All of his efforts weren't as successful as the wood chopping and the milking. Papa and Mama praised him highly and Papa commended especially his drum playing. Indeed, he seemed to have an unsuspected ear for rhythm.

Spring came to Salt Lake City and some of the other lower towns and cities as early as February sometimes, but it wasn't until the last of April that the final bits of clinging ice could be kicked off the cement sidewalks on Coleman's block. After that ice was gone, it seemed that everything greened rapidly. With the greening, Papa began to get some feeling in the leg we had taken turns rubbing every night. By June he was out of bed, and though he always wore heavy wool socks, even in summer, to keep his feet warm, there was little to remind us of his winter in bed except a limp which was noticeable only when he hurried.

Marybeth graduated from high school and went into nurse's training at Idaho Falls. Jeanne, though always one of an inseparable quartet of girls her age, seemed lost without Marybeth. "It's the nights," she told me. "I get by fine in the daytime, there is so much to do. But at night when I turn over to tell Marybeth everything, it's just awful, Prilla." I knew how that was. June and July had been my listeners and when they had gone Emily was not too young to lend an empathic ear, but now there were only three of us. Jeremy, freed finally from tyranny, blissfully boiled around in exciting activity. He'd discovered the football team (to watch; he was not old enough to play) and he was making plans. He'd made friends with the director of the school band, mowing his lawn faithfully every Saturday. He'd fallen in love with Norma Clyde and he'd found out he was probably the best-looking boy in our end of town. Scouting, the only one of his activities that had Papa's full approval, took up all the rest of his time. He milked in the morning, but Papa could not wait for his regretful excuses at night. There was always something that held him at school.

The house was much too big, it seemed, and Mama, always looking for ways to add to our income, decided to take in boarders. Our boarders were nice ones, two schoolteachers, Reba Tew and Mabel Cox, come from their hot southern Utah towns for the first time into our long-wintered climate. Mama repapered the boys' bedroom, made fresh dotted Swiss curtains, and favored them with Grandma's crocheted bedspread. Papa built a bookcase, and we put Grandma's and Grandpa's rocking chairs in their room.

They were quite happy, and did not seem inconvenienced that the necessary was located out through the backyard gate, around the chicken yard, past the coops, and behind them.

Up until now we'd limited our barnyard animals to the usual, but Johnny Winterrose, for a change, owed Papa some money for work done and he talked Papa into, as he had been talked into, taking a goat in exchange for services rendered. Our goat, named Billy of course, had the traditional billy-goatish temper. Mama warned the schoolmarms about him, and explained that he was tethered out of butting reach of the toilet and that they should stay on the path. One night the teachers had to go out at the same time. Reba Tew couldn't wait her turn, so she went behind the chicken coop. The sight of those flipped-up skirts was too much for Billy. He came out of the dark like a battering ram and knocked poor Miss Tew sprawling. The schoolteachers screamed, and Papa and Mama ran outside to the rescue. Papa, as any of us would have expected, thought the situation was hilarious. Every time his eyes met those of the bruise-bottomed teacher, his mustache began to twitch and his eyes twinkled. So Mama's boarders found a place with a modern bathroom. "I'm sure you understand—the convenience and . . . all . . ." And Mama did.

She tried to talk Papa into putting a bathroom in the house, but he said he couldn't afford it and, besides, it was more trouble than it was worth. Maybe it was the inside bathroom that folks used then as a status symbol. If so, we were poor.

Probably Mama was right when she accused all of us of having warped senses of humor. I know that when Kathryn, July's first-born, expected her first date (it was an unfortunate time—at one of the gatherings of the clan), Jeanne said seriously: "Now when your young man arrives, I'll run up-stairs and flush the toilet, just so he'll know we have one inside!" We laughed uncontrollably, but poor Kathryn looked at us with bewilderment and (her mother had taught her well) a patient acceptance.

Papa, not so much for sayings as for Biblical quotations, frequently warned us: "Lay not up treasures of silver and gold that moths can corrupt and thieves break in and steal." And joking, but with sharp grains of truth growing in and around the words: "Your Mama and I have left you a fine heritage. The heritage of going without!"

Oh, how much they left us in that heritage. I suppose that he knew what he was leaving, saying it as he did, but we didn't know. We thought it was another crust of his dry humor.

[CHAPTER TWENTY-ONE]

I DON'T KNOW whether it was the result of our "poor winter" or whether Jeremy was built on the principle of double-acting baking powder. Suddenly he started doing things. During that winter, as I've said, he learned to play the drums, and in his sophomore year made the school band. He tried out for drum major in his junior year and made it. He should have. He marched around our yard with a broom for hours at a time. Papa thought it was a rather silly occupation to be carried on with such great dignity, but he wouldn't say anything to discourage Jeremy at anything! The first time Jeremy marched down Main Street at the head of the high-school band he was repaid for his forbearance. But Jeremy hadn't changed all that much!

Growing up the center of our garden were five full-spreading Jonathan apple trees. I have yet to see fruit to compare in size and crisp perfection with the apples they bore each fall. Each morning, when they ripened, I chose two, one for myself and one to give away to the first friend I met that day. This was one of the soul-satisfying pleasures of my life. It must have been equally so with the others, for I was not the only one who visited the garden each morning.

Jeremy had been taking a course in "ag" (I suppose that this had some such dignified name as botany or animal husbandry or maybe agriculture), and he would always take the word of a fresh turned college graduate to Papa's or any other experienced farmer's any hour of any day. Jeremy decided, after a discussion with his "prof," who had never seen our trees, that the apple trees needed pruning. One morning before any of us waked, Jeremy pruned them, to surprise Papa.

When Papa saw the carnage in the garden, he shouted words that I had no idea he knew, and they ripped out in a stream that sent Mama scurrying outside in her long-sleeved gown with her night braids flying. Budding limbs lay slaughtered on the ground. Mama went back in the house to bed and stayed all morning. I sat down in the dew-wet grass and wept. None of the trees bore fruit again except for a few wizened atrocities that resembled ground cherries in their puckered brownness.

I don't know how rapidly Papa would have recovered or forgiven Jeremy, but he didn't have much time to stay mad. Jeremy and the band went to California and, right on Movietone News, Jeremy twirled our little town onto the map. He marched that band to victory over all the competition from bands all over the United States and he was a celebrity. There was no stopping him now.

This was the spring of Jeanne's graduation from high school, but college was out of the question for her. Girls could only get work in offices and stores or train as nurses. Marybeth wrote and asked Jeanne to join her, but Jeanne hesitated, and before she had time to decide, Antony wrote and begged for her to come to them. Emily Ellen was having difficulty in a pregnancy and she was homesick. Antony felt that Jeanne would be the tonic that Emily needed. So Mama let her go, more tearfully than she had freed the rest of us.

Her going would have been much harder to bear, I think, except that Jeremy filled the house with his football team, his basketball team, his drum major's corps, and his Scout troop. There was always a pair of bony ankles sticking out of every chair, couch, porch, and step in the house. We had other troubles, too.

Mama had one of her dreams, the last one, and she was frantically insistent that Papa take action. This time it was about Rachel Ann.

"I dreamed," said Mama, "that Rollo came, limping on crutches. He did not smile, not once! He said that Rachel Ann was in California somewhere and he asked me to find her. He said the child had been ill and that Alice neglected her and left her alone. The child had been ill treated and Alice was not a fit mother for his daughter."

"Kate, we can't do anything about this. Alice is the child's legal guardian. She is the executor of Rollo's will. We haven't a leg to stand on."

"Dave," Mama said, "Rollo stood by my bed and looked

down at me and begged: 'Mama, please go get my little girl!'
I promised that I would. And if you won't go, Dave, I
will."

So Papa went to Salt Lake City to inquire of the Indus-
trial Commission about Alice's whereabouts. Insurance
checks were mailed to Rollo's widow from there. The
Commission, working through the Red Cross, found the
child, and Mama was right again. Rachel Ann was taken
away, without any dissent from Alice, and sent to us.

"I'll not have the worry of insecurity again," said Mama,
thinking of Boot and Frances. "And if Alice is not a fit
mother for the child, then Rachel Ann must be ours."

So reluctantly, for Rachel Ann's benefit, Papa and Mama
went to court to adopt her. They had no difficulty. Alice
signed the adoption papers without protest. It was Rachel
Ann who protested.

"I don't want to be adopted," she told the judge. "I'll
stay with them, but I don't want to be adopted." And her
tears streaked the front of her new red taffeta dress.

When Dyke Palmer had driven me to meet her at the
Union Pacific depot in Salt Lake, she knew me immediately.
She wasn't hard to find, a lonely but staunchly independent
little seven-year-old with a tag around her neck like a
C.O.D. parcel.

"You're my Aunt Prilla, aren't you?"

"Yes." I bent down to kiss her and she allowed me to do
it.

"I remember you."

"You were pretty small when you were up home last," I
said, doubtfully, and she looked at me calmly.

"I remember you, though."

She didn't talk much on the way home, just looked out at the canyon scenery, and I was afraid that she'd feel I was forcing answers from her if I questioned her. I remembered how I used to feel about grownups and their questions.

When we drove into town, she suddenly came to life.

"Before you get to Grandpa's there's a church and then you turn up." At least Alice had described us well to Rachel Ann, but I was not sure of that when Rachel identified the church and the turning and our house as we neared it. The house had made its mark on her, too. She had remembered.

Mama came hurrying out to hug and kiss Rachel, and Papa patted her head and led her by the hand up the front-porch steps.

"Looks like the house will have a child for some time yet to come, Kate," Papa said, and smiled. He was, as I was, thinking again of Mama's wish.

Rachel Ann seemed to settle slowly, like a kitten going round and round to find the softest place in its pillow and then finally settling down. She made no fuss at all, just watched us with her quiet eyes. Not for a long time did I see the flash and sparkle of the smile that marked her as Rollo's child.

She questioned me as I prepared for my wedding.

"You think you're going to like being a stepmother?"

"I'm sure that I am. I like children. I've always been around them."

"Are you going to have some babies, too?"

"I hope so!"

"Are you going to like your babies better than the old kids, when you have them?"

"No, I'm not, Rachel Ann." And then I told her about the house and how it always made room for everyone. I told her of Frances and Boot and Marybeth and Jeremy and how they were Mama and Papa's children, too.

"I didn't know Jeremy was borrowed. Is that the same as adopted."

"Not quite. Adopted makes it solider, more like being owned. You're my little sister, too. Do you like that better?"

"I don't know whether I do nor not," she said honestly. "It's rather odd to be your own aunt. I'm Rachel Ann's Aunt Rachel Ann. But it's kind of funny." And she laughed with Rollo's chuckle.

The adoption and my wedding took place the same week. Mama and Rachel went down to the judge's offices to get the papers. Rachel was sitting on the porch when Dyke and I left home in a flurry of kisses and good-byes, although I was moving only two blocks away.

"What is that, Rachel?" I asked her. She was clasping something tight in her hand. She held it out to me.

"Why it's a five-dollar gold piece! Where on earth did you get it?"

"Judge Hatch gave it to me for being a nice girl and giving up my mother."

And suddenly tears welled out of my heart and into my eyes. "Always," Mama had warned us, "you must be prepared to take the bitter with the sweet."

I included Rachel Ann in all the picnics and special things that we planned for our family and I felt very maternal toward her, but she was always a bit aloof. She baffled me. It was not that I did not love her, that all of us did not love her. It was more that she could not accept the fact that we did. But in the rush of our lives we had not time to pick a steep and misty way into the heart and mind of just one child. There were so many other people who claimed a part of us.

One afternoon I had baked an extra-large cake, as Mama used to in her big dripper. Too much for us, cut and layered, I wanted to share it with Papa and Mama and Rachel. I had just time to deliver it before Dyke would be home for dinner.

There was no one in the house, but someone was home, for the fire had been recently replenished. I went out to the dooryard gate and called: "Mama? Rachel Ann?"

I heard a rustling in the granary and opened the door. Rachel Ann was rising from her wooden-box chair. She had been playing tea party. Her house was neatly arranged inside the big, oddly square box that had so horrified me when I had first seen it. My voice high and cross with shock, I scolded her. "Rachel Ann! What are you doing, playing in that box! Can't you find a better place on such a nice sunny day. Go out into the Circle. That makes a lovely playhouse. Here. I'll help you carry your things, and I've brought you some cake."

"No, Aunt Prilla. I'll stay here. I like this place." And she explained to me: "It was my daddy's, you know, and it is the only place that holds me tight."

It would have only shocked Rachel to pull her from the box, to hold her and croon over her, as I was so impatient to do over the baby that was coming to Dyke and me, so I patted her firm little hand where it lightly rested on the smooth side of the big box and I started to leave before she saw my tears.

"Good-bye, Aunt Prilla. Thanks for the cake. Is it all right if I cut it before Grandma comes?"

"It sure is, honey, I brought it for you. Don't let the fire go out, unless you want to gather chips to start a new one." I hoped that my voice was as sweetly calm as hers. But I knew then that Rachel Ann had faced her problems and accepted them and that she would be a sturdy blessing for Papa and Mama as they grew old.

I went home almost every afternoon and helped Mama with the canning, which had to be done when the fruits and vegetables came on, so I was there when Papa destroyed Jeremy's summer work.

Jeremy had decided that he was going to go on to college and from his band work he had been offered a scholarship to the state agricultural college. The scholarship would cover books and tuition. He had to make enough money to pay for his living expenses. He and another ambitious, scheming young man had worked all that summer thinning beets. There is hardly harder work. They lived on rice and Mama's baskets of food when we managed to get them delivered.

They saved almost every cent of their money and bought several five-gallon jugs of bootleg whiskey. With bottles they had salvaged from behind the city jail they planned to go into a profitable business. Each pint of whiskey was to be sold (and they had orders for nearly all of it), at a prohibition price, for almost what they had paid for five gallons. The profit, divided equally, would keep them both, they figured, until they could find part-time work to finance their living expenses at school. But Papa found the whiskey.

Cleaning out the raspberry patches at a time when no reasonable man would ever think to clean out raspberry patches, he came upon the bottles and the jugs and he knew immediately what they were intended for. He poured out the whiskey and recapped the jugs, so as to make it clear that the act was deliberate.

Jeremy discovered his loss when he and Perry, his friend, and about eight prospective customers sauntered to the berry patch. He came running to the house, an empty jug dangling from each thumb.

"Who did it?" he choked. "Who did it?"

Mama knew. I could see that Papa had told her to keep quiet. I knew because I knew Papa, and Jeremy didn't have to be told.

Jeremy was hysterical, swearing much as Papa had done the morning of the rape of the apple trees. He was raving about his aching back, about living on boiled rice (the only thing he knew how to cook), and the lost summer money. "Besides . . ."

Papa came in just then and Jeremy swallowed whatever he had been about to say and hid his red-faced belligerence behind the comic section. I knew that Papa had heard Jeremy because of the way his mustache twitched. I knew also that Jeremy wouldn't dare say a word. He never did.

Just before Jeremy left for college, he was awarded the first Eagle Scout badge to be given in our county. There were many other awards being given at the time and the scoutmaster made a big night of it. One of the members of the General Board of the Mutual Improvement Association was asked out to the Stake House to make the awards. I don't know who gave the board member Jeremy's history, but certainly it was someone who did not know him very well. It could have been Jeremy himself!

Papa and Mama sat well down in front. Dyke and I were there. The twins and their husbands had driven up from Salt

Lake for the evening. We were so proud of Jeremy. He'd started out so clumsily and had turned, or was turning, out so well.

When it was Jeremy's time to march across the stage (his band leading had given him incredible poise), the visiting dignitary made quite a speech. He spoke of how the award called for perseverance and determination and hard work. He set Jeremy up as an example to all the other boys of our county, if not the state—if not the nation, because after observing his accomplishments in the face of such odds, they, the other boys, could have no valid excuse for lack of achievement.

I could see the rest of the family were as bewildered as I. How had the speaker found out about Jeremy's difficulties? We thought them to be a family secret. How many other people's trees had he pruned!

"This splendid young man," said the speaker, reaching up to place his hand paternally on Jeremy's broad shoulder, "never had a helping hand. He has done this alone, by himself. He is an orphan boy!" That was why Papa and Mama had not been called to stand to sit with their son. I had wondered, but apparently they hadn't.

What else the speaker said, none of us heard, for the shock the words gave Mama and Papa was so great that Papa grunted as if someone had hit him, hard, in the stomach. Mama put her shawl over her head and hurried out into the night where no one could see her face, and I know that few things have hurt them worse.

I don't know what Jeremy thought about the presentation. It is quite possible he was so excited that he did not even hear the words. He never mentioned them to me. I did not discuss it with him, and if Papa and Mama's enthusiasm was not as vocal as usual, Jeremy might well have thought it was because they were getting older and tired easily. No one ever mentioned it. There are some things that cannot bear discussion.

[CHAPTER TWENTY-TWO]

THE HIGH POINT, the culmination of the good life is not always pinpointed. In our town it was. Mama started talking about her Golden Wedding on her fortieth anniversary. I never knew Papa to take Mama out to dinner. Indeed, there was no such place to take her, if they had been so inclined, and for such tomfoolery they certainly were not. I never knew him to give her a gift, not even for Christmas. It was enough for them both that all the children were given a package to open and a stocking to empty.

We gave them gifts as we grew older. We would go together to try to make it something worthwhile. One prosperous year, Jeanne and Davy shipped a new dining-room set via the Creeper, and after Davy had paid one of his two brief visits, he sent them the finest console radio he could find in California. The radio came at a time when it was still a novelty in the living room and a miracle in Papa's mind. The novelty wore away, but the miracle, for Papa, never did. He never switched it on that he did not marvel at the wisdom of God and the cleverness of man. I surmised that the radio was Davy's way of saying he was sorry. However, this time, he paid the freight charges.

High in the top of Mama's narrow closet were two big boxes. Each year after Christmas, she would climb up to deposit her Christmas cards in one of these. There were birthday cards, letters from special friends, the shiny black-and-gold "In Memoriam" cards that marked the passing of friends and relatives, Rollo's army uniform with one of Rachel's baby bonnets tucked in one of its pockets, and hundreds of pictures. They were mostly tintypes and bronze-toned stiffnesses of newly-marrieds, the husband with his hand proprietarily on the wing of his wife's chair or, more intimately, on her shoulder. In the pictures taken a few years earlier, it was the husband who sat, his wife standing primly corseted and basqued and bustled at his side. None of us knew these women who wore their hair drawn severely back from their foreheads or these men whose mustaches outdid Papa's pride. But they were friends. Relegated to the top of the closet, perhaps, but still part of Mama's and Papa's lives.

This afternoon, Mama reluctantly left Davy at home alone while she did her beat. Although her hours with Davy were precious, she had her duty toward her Relief Society teaching and duty is a most powerful master.

Davy, always restless, decided to clean out the disgraceful mess in the top of the closet. He had spent several of his recent years on a submarine and had learned to abhor clutter and the hoarding of objects that had no function. At least this was the way Mama excused him. Now, methodically, he cleaned. With only a cursory glance to see if the photographs were of anyone he recognized, he tossed them. The few he knew he piled on the dinning-room table; the rest he threw into the greedy little potbellied stove. Between the two of them they demolished almost fifty years.

Mama had stopped by my house to ask us over for dinner and I walked home with her. We were surprised to see smoke forking from the front-room chimney, and Mama, intuitive, ran up the walk and up the front-room steps.

"Oh, Davy!" She sat down in Grandma's little black rocker and rocked swiftly, covering her mouth and chin with her spread fingers. "Oh my, Davy!"

"What do you think you're doing?" I asked him, and then he seemed to have an inkling of what he had done.

"Hell, I just cleaned out a lot of this mouse fodder. Do you know, Mama had stuff stored in that closet she's had since she and Papa were married? She needed someone to help her clear it out."

" And you did!"

"Never mind, Prilla. Never mind," Mama interrupted. "He didn't know."

"Didn't know what?" he demanded. "None of this dusty old stuff was any good. I kept anything that was."

And there was no use telling him that he'd thrown away the priceless tangible bits of Mama's and Papa's memories. The Christmas cards from Aunt Mag, which she had painted and versed herself, because she could not afford to buy a gift. Mama would not have sold these for food or clothing. The cards from Boot and Rollo, the few letters from Davy himself, which she so valued, and which were the first to go. The pictures of friends long dead, of babies grown up now and scattered to the far ends of the earth. There, in the top of her closet, Mama had stored a record of her life, and in one afternoon Davy, who found no value to a keepsake and roamed the world looking for something to keep with him, had destroyed her years of sentiment.

"Slush! Now she can store her quilts up there. Put the space to some good use."

I was tempted to retort, but, as Mama said, "there is none so blind as he who will not see." It was hard to keep from being cool when I kissed my brother good-bye at the end of his leave.

"I'm sorry if I burned some of that stuff that Mama wanted," he said gruffly. "It just seemed too damned silly, old verses to the dead, letters you can't read. Who wants it?"

But Mama held him to her and kissed him, for it was doubtful, always doubtful, that she would see him again. The other side of the world was almost as far away as the star of Kolob.

It was right after this visit that Davy sent the radio, and Papa, though he worried for fear the electric bill would exceed the one-dollar minimum, sat crouched in the little armless red rocker that had been Emily Ellen's, and twisted the dial and listened to the static and said, shaking his head: "That's a sure sign. There's a storm at sea somewhere." Then he and Mama would sit and wonder if Davy was riding a ship in that storm, and if ever he could come home again.

Davy didn't make it home for the Golden Wedding, but the rest of us did. The anniversary was in July, a wonderful month in our mountains. Now the roses were in high bloom, the purple-blue delphiniums stretched to peer over the tops of picket fences. There were phlox ("flocks" suited them much better) in pink, lavender, white, and deep rose red. There were varicolored cosmos which thoroughly disproved someone's idea that certain color combinations were not compatible. There were bachelor's buttons, the old-fashioned ones in soft delft blue and more daring ones in a brave purply pink. These banked the gate on either side and Papa, as he passed, always stopped a moment to select a special one for his buttonhole.

For this special anniversary the flowers outbloomed themselves. In our own yard there were almost enough to decorate the huge amusement hall where we were going to welcome Papa and Mama's friends. Mama fussed. "Why not have it here at home?" But Antony, Emily Ellen's strong shoulder, said simply: "It's the only place in town big enough unless we rent the Fair Grounds, but they don't have a roof and it could rain."

"You're making too much of this," Mama said, pleased. "Why, half our friends are dead by now. I'm going to be embarrassed with that big hall and only a few people in one end of it."

"You get prettied up," Antony told her. "We'll do all the worrying."

For weeks before coming home, Emily Ellen and Jeanne had baked white fruitcakes and packed them in tins for transporting. They ordered ice cream from Ad Averett on the day they arrived. Out in back of his confectionery, on the day of the wedding, he had boys turning his big freezers. For no place else could you buy such ice cream, hand-mixed with eggs and cream and drifts of flavor. You smelled it whenever you entered the confectionery and it enticed you to one of the little round tables with its curved wire Coca-Cola chairs. Ad made gallons of punch, too, and delivered it himself in his truck, packed in ice, to be unloaded as it was served. He sent two husky, muscled young men to unload it and to run errands if we needed them.

We made dozens of tiny cookies, and I beat blisters onto my wooden-spoon hand, but my blisters were only a few of many. June and July baked. Marybeth baked. Jeanne baked. Frances drove determinedly down from Idaho loaded to the tops of her car seats with boxes of cookies and affectionate kisses that she bestowed on everyone who came near her.

Zion had grown. There was not an empty space in our age calendar. Marybeth's teen-aged daughter (she, like me, had married a widower with a child to be loved) and two curly-haired toddlers, Emily Ellen's three, widely spaced, browned from a California sun, Dyke's and mine, June and July's five, who were constantly queried by the others: "Kathryn, I know that your mother is Aunt July, but which one is she?" Tyler's children were teen-agers and were taken for granted as pairs of legs meant to run errands. Rachel Ann found importance in her sister-niece-aunt status and was unusually dutiful. All of them had been admonished, I know, that "Grandma thinks children should be seen and not heard." What a delightful, sensible, saving admonition!

Without any "You do that" or "I'll do this," things fitted. Jeremy, finally achieving mental and muscular coordination, chopped wood, showing off his muscles before the shy and admiring new wife. Both of them had graduated from college that June. The little boys filled the woodbox. We cleaned house, slipping easily into tasks that had been ours when we were girls. Emily Ellen and Jeanne and Antony took over the decorating of the big hall. Antony went purposefully to visit the owners of luxuriant flower gardens. He had previously marked these on a drive around town. Without asking, which was against the rules, somehow he managed to leave each garden with his arms full of blossoms grown for the Fair exhibits.

The company came. Mama's brothers and sisters. The in-laws and the uncles and the aunts and the cousins. The straw mattresses stretched out into the yard at night and were stacked neatly against the fence during the day.

Mama had her hair done for the first time at the beauty parlor. She would not go unless Rachel Ann went to sit with her in that strange place. When they came home, Jeanne combed out the store-bought curls and combed in the soft natural waves that were Mama's own.

"Hmph," she sniffed. "All that time and money wasted, and I don't look a whit different than I did when I went down there."

"But you look like Mama," said Jeanne, and we approved.

"Hmph. Seems you could look like something special once in your life!"

"Pretty is as pretty does!" Marybeth smirked.

Antony was right. We could have used the Fair Grounds, if they had had a roof. The amusement hall filled with people, who lined up all the way down the block to shake hands and hug and kiss and reminisce briefly with Aunt Kate and Uncle Dave. To take the place of the dear departed ones were their children and their children's children.

For the Millers, who had moved out of the house two blocks down from us, came the Townsends, little Mrs.

Townsend with tears in her eyes. She told us: "You know, I was so homesick. Moving into this strange little community. I'm a big-city girl from back East and apartment houses and neighbors you never know. I was sitting at the kitchen table reading a letter from my mother and being pregnant and crying. Here came sweet Uncle Dave with a bouquet of flowers out of his garden and a little green nubbly squash for our dinner. He came right in as though he was quite at home . . . and of course he was. He'd spent many hours in my kitchen before I was born. He told me about the fine babies that'd been born in this house and how the man who lived here before us wrote poetry that was published. He told me that he always tried to visit fresh brides and fresh mothers and the fresh bereaved, for these were the ones who appreciated flowers most. After Uncle Dave left, the house, somehow, was mine and the town was mine and I belonged."

And a serious young man leaving the next day for a Mission: "Uncle Dave, until you shaved off your mustache that time and nobody knew you, I thought you were Santa Claus. You always smiled and waved when we called you that. It was a blow to find that you were just Uncle Dave Woodrow, really."

And the doctor. To no one in particular, to all of us, except Papa: "If every Mormon was like this old man, I'd a had to be a Mormon. If I called on him at three o'clock in the middle of the night, at nine the next morning, if he could hobble, he'd be down to pay the bill. Half the time when I hurried my fastest, I'd find him ahead of me already administering to the sick. At first," he chuckled, "I got mad. What was I doin' there with him and Brother Duke already tellin' the folks that their sick would recover! Then I got so I felt sort of a team spirit. But I never once beat him to the patient. Tell me, Uncle Dave, how did you do it, you lived farther away many times than I did."

Papa grinned widely and shook his head, but Mama looked exasperated.

"I'll tell you his secret, Doctor. He hasn't been undressed except to take a bath for most of the fifty years we've been married. When folks'd come to the bedroom window and knock and call 'Uncle Dave' to come and pray for the sick, all he ever had to do was to pull on his pants and shoes and put a bridle on his riding horse. He kept one saddled at night. Sometimes he didn't even bother to light the lamp."

"You didn't even undress?"

"I was always a slow dresser. And it was foolish. There have been some pretty sick folks and I couldn't keep 'em waiting."

Until that moment I had never thought it odd that whenever I went into the bedroom when Papa was in bed, he was always wearing his shirt and, yes, even his bow tie. And then I realized why he slept the way he did, sitting upright almost on high pillows, on his back. I had thought it was for comfort, but it was to keep his shirt from getting wrinkled!

"Papa," I asked during a pause in the greeting, "weren't you uncomfortable all these years?"

"Got so it was the only way I could sleep. Anyway, it was a lot easier than tying that bow tie every time!"

And our favorite family neighbor, who was the daughter to Mama and Papa when none of us could be. "Your parents are so dear to us. Both my girls, Barbara and Evelyn, you know, had to write themes in college about the person who had most influenced their lives. Both of them wrote, without mentioning it to the other, about your Papa. These are my children . . . you can well imagine what these dear old people mean to me."

The Governor came. Not as an invited guest. He came up to speak to a Democratic rally some optimist had scheduled for that night in the Stake House. There was no one there except the Mayor and the marshal, and when the Governor asked what had happened, they told him.

"Everybody in the county over twenty-one, including our wives, is at the Golden Wedding. So the Governor came, too, and asked politely for a couple of minutes, if we could spare them, of our program time. The grandchildren, who were the program, gratefully granted his request and the Governor scrupulously used only his two minutes.

He said he was delighted to join us in paying tribute to these two fine Democrats, and with this brief and brilliant campaign he carried our heretofore Republican county in the election the next week.

Papa danced and sang "The Man on the Flying Trapeze," and Mama and Papa danced briefly, for me another first. I had never before seen them dance together. He held her as carefully as he carried his bouquets and flowers, or his grandchildren when he carried them up to the front of the church to give them a name. It was a lovely moment; the women were dabbing their eyes with their handkerchiefs and the men coughed and blew their noses.

Rachel Ann and Kathryn came to tell us that Emily Ellen's and June's young sons were selling the punch, in used cups, to thirsty dancers, just around the bend of the cloakroom. We put them out of business and set up another punch bowl where we could watch the punch tenders. We would have sent all the little ones home to bed, but we could not bear to leave to take them and no one else was willing either, so we made beds on the benches and put our little ones to sleep while we danced and sang and visited into the cool dawn hours.

I am sure that Papa told Mama that he loved her that night as he danced with her, for he bent his head to her and whispered and I thought perhaps from the way he looked at her that he told her she was beautiful, too. I came to know this for certain, but it was not for a long time after the Golden Wedding.

Mama had fallen over the up-jog step of the parlor and had broken her hip. It was, as she had predicted so very long ago, to be the death of her. She was sitting in the sun where I had placed her in her rocking chair. Her hair was white, her face lined, her eyes shadowed, clearly recognizing only Papa, but always Papa.

He came from a brisk trip to the post office and she saw him, brightening, as he approached the gate. As he passed through, he picked a rosebud and, coming to her slowly, tucked it into her hair. I was standing behind the screen door and he did not see me.

She reached to caress his cheek in that same gentle motion that I had seen at Rollo's grave. Catching the hand and holding it against his face, he said tenderly: "Ah, Kate, when I married you I thought you were the most beautiful girl in the county, but now I know that you are the most beautiful woman in the world."

I stood in my private shadows and wept for the exquisite completeness of their lives together. They had known it all.

Pain enough to appreciate its absence, bitterness enough to appreciate the sweet, sorrow enough to appreciate happiness. They had had their share of miracles and, with them, we had our share, too.

COME OVER HERE, MY SON

Come over here, my son, said dear old Dad,
You're old enough to know a thing or two.
I've wanted to tell you what is good and bad,
And I'll explain the difference to you.
You're going to need some good advice someday,
And these words come straight from my heart.
Take the road that's straight and follow right along,
You'll be happy when we have to part.

Keep away from the gals and the good-fellow pals,
As long as you've got money they'll be true.
Treat everyone fair. Always be on the square,
And everybody everywhere will welcome you.
Settle down in life with a sweet little wife,
Remember that the day that you were blessed,
You had sunshine and flowers and many happy hours,
On the road to happiness.

Now think this over, son, and don't forget,
That what your daddy tells you now is true.
Just do as I say and you will ne'er regret
And good luck will always follow you.
You're going to need some good advice someday,
And these words come straight from my heart.
Take the road that's straight and follow right along,
You'll be happy when we have to part.

Keep away from the gals and the good-fellow pals,
As long as you've got money, they'll be true.
Treat everyone fair. Always be on the square,
And good luck will always follow you.
Settle down in life with a sweet little wife
Remember that the day that you were blessed,
You had sunshine and flowers and many happy hours,
On the road to happiness.

AUTHOR UNKNOWN

A NOTE ON THE TYPE

THE TEXT of this book was set on the Linotype in *Janson*, a recutting made direct from type cast from matrices long thought to have been made by the Dutchman Anton Janson, who was a practicing type founder in Leipzig during the years 1668–87. However, it has been conclusively demonstrated that these types are actually the work of Nicholas Kis (1650–1702), a Hungarian, who most probably learned his trade from the master Dutch type founder Dirk Voskens. The type is an excellent example of the influential and sturdy Dutch types that prevailed in England up to the time William Caslon developed his own incomparable designs from these Dutch faces.

Composed, printed, and bound by
The Haddon Craftsmen, Scranton, Pennsylvania
Typography and binding design by
GUY FLEMING

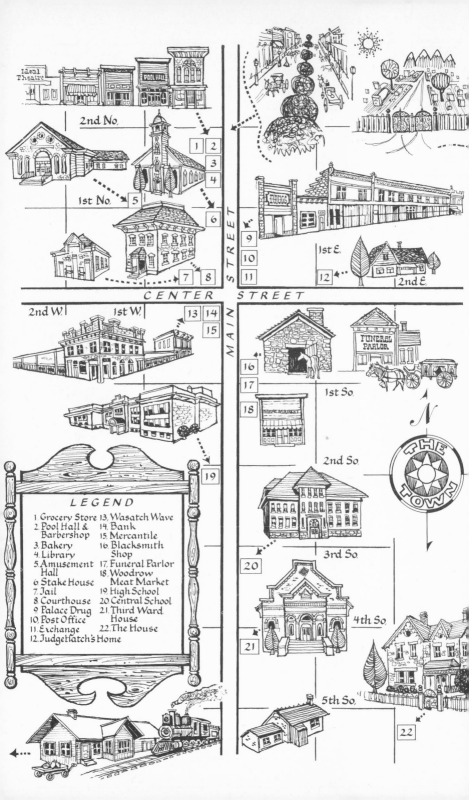

LEGEND

1. Grocery Store
2. Pool Hall & Barbershop
3. Bakery
4. Library
5. Amusement Hall
6. Stake House
7. Jail
8. Courthouse
9. Palace Drug
10. Post Office
11. Exchange
12. Judge Hatch's Home
13. Wasatch Wave
14. Bank
15. Mercantile
16. Blacksmith Shop
17. Funeral Parlor
18. Woodrow Meat Market
19. High School
20. Central School
21. Third Ward House
22. The House